# SPERM BANDITS

## DOTUN ADEBAYO

Published by
The X Press
PO Box 25694
London, N17 6FP
Tel: 020 8801 2100
Fax: 020 8885 1322
E-mail: vibes@xpress.co.uk

Distributed in UK by Turnaround Distribution
Unit 3, Olympia Trading Estate, Coburg Road, London N22 6TZ
Tel: 020 8829 3000
Fax: 020 8881 5088

Dotun Adebayo is the author of
*Can I Have My Balls Back Please?*
He is also a regular on Radio 5 Live and on BBC
London 94.9 where he hosts his own show.
He lives in north London with his wife
and two young daughters.

*Scientists say that through DNA testing they can prove that women came to be on this planet many thousand of years before the male...*

# SPERM BANDITS

## A HARD MAN IS GOOD TO FIND

I knew that heading would grab your attention. Honestly, you lot are so bleeding predictable. Any mention of sex and your eyes spark up like a shot. Well, hard luck. Because this isn't about male sexual organs. Not entirely anyway. More precisely, it's about that most precious of human resources — sperm.

Let me make one thing clear from the giddyup — I am now a happily settled family man. My main concern in life is what's on TV. My interests include DIY, and I listen to talk radio all day long. Since my missus separated my genitals from my morals ('Can I Have My Balls Back *Please?*') I do not cheat, nor do I have a desire to cheat (unless someone makes me). My sexperience is a product of the past, but after all these years who knows where the product of my sex has ended up?

Your guess is as good as mine. I remember my first sexual encounter and I remember my most recent, but somewhere in the middle is a huge blur of faces and names that I couldn't possibly remember even if you held a shotgun to my balls. That sperm could be anywhere!

I'm not talking just any old sperm, but the good stuff, the perfect sperm. You know, the kind that certain women are prepared to lose their minds for. The star semen that a happily married woman might even commit adultery for. Let's face it, every man is a walking gene pool, and women generally go for the most sought-after male genes they can lay their hands on. Once they're identified as the best genes available, some woman will zoom in with all the precision of a guided missile in hot pursuit. Whether it's Madonna choosing a fine physical specimen to father her child, or Jodie Foster picking through the sperm bank records to find the right combination of brains, health and stamina to father hers.

It's always gone on, but never so brazenly or proudly as today. I don't see women rushing the ugly geezers and the blokes with fat heads or coconut bonces, not when they realise that their pickney's going to look like that. But I do see women rushing movie stars, pop stars and soccer stars for a taste of their DNA. Admittedly one or two damn ugly politicians and billionaires get rushed too, but that's strictly on a boopsie trip. Generally, if you've got a healthy skin, good hair, a firm batty, broad shoulders and a little bit of charm and intelligence, you're going to get rushed. It's a risky strategy, but a lot of women are prepared to take that risk in choosing a man/men to get pregnant by, because a woman is looking for genes which, in combination with her own, will produce attractive and successful pickney.

So when it comes to looking for the perfect genes, these women don't have a problem enticing guys to 'give it up'. Hell, yeah! If you ask me, women have got too much choice when it comes to genes. All they've got to do is put on a little make-up, get their hair done down at the salon and whistle, and some of the best genes in the area will start cummin'. I don't mean just the young, free and singles either. If a married man has got some dope genes, he stands a good chance of getting his end away, whether he's prepared to desert his wife or not. After all, a woman's not necessarily choosing someone she wants to spend the rest of her life with, or even to raise her children with. She's primarily interested in the reproductive potential. And if she can't get the best, then she'll settle for second best, third best... A hard core of women will go even further. SPERM BANDITS!

Sperm bandits have been around for hundreds of years. Sadly. Yet most men still don't know what's going on. As far as we're concerned, these women are dressing criss and making themselves look good and purring sexy words into our ears simply out of the goodness of their hearts. It doesn't even enter our tiny heads to think that it's anything to do with cunning, guile, daring and desire to get at the 'right' genes. We don't even stop and wonder why a woman we've never met before is prepared to walk the tightrope of abuse and disease by spreading her legs wide for us. Let's face it, when we've got our mind on sex, the last thing we're going to be saying to ourselves is 'Rather brave of her to let me dip my wick when she knows what a dog I am and most dogs carry fleas.'

I know, those happily married men with three kids and a people carrier amongst you will be saying, 'At least I know where all my kids are.' Yeah, you know WHERE they are, but do you know WHO they are? Take a close look at your pickney. That'll be an even closer look when I tell you that, up to ten per cent of children in Britain are not the children of their supposed fathers. In other words, there are a lot of women out there walking around with a helluva big secret. Fellas, take a close look at your first and last pickney. 'Cause they're the ones most likely not to be yours. The second child's definitely yours, though. Ugly same way.

If you're a working class man without qualifications, then (sorry, mate) the chances of your kids not being yours could be as high as thirty per cent. Not only that, the REAL father to your kids is probably some rich geezer who went to Eton and Cambridge. I kid you not, blondes prefer gentlemen with a bit of high class genes in 'em.

High class or low class, more and more I'm discovering cases where men claim they've become fathers not because they chose to, or even because of an accident, but because they trusted women who said they were taking precautions.

Men like ex-Wimbledon tennis ace Boris Becker and a growing number of ordinary men I've been reading about are not running away from their responsibilities. They're saying that having sex with someone doesn't mean you're signing up for fatherhood.

Does a man have the right to choose how and when he becomes a father? Not when there's a SPERM BANDIT about.

# CAN I HAVE MY SPERM BACK
## *PLEASE?*

*Jonathan Evans, a high-flying young businessman, met Corinne Tindall at a club in Leamington Spa, shortly after he split up from his wife. The last thing he wanted was a baby, so he used a condom every time. It wasn't long before Corinne dropped a bombshell — she was pregnant.*

*"I was shocked," said Jonathan, "but I accepted it because I know condoms are only ninety per cent safe."*

*Just as he was coming to terms with the idea of fatherhood, Corinne revealed the incredible truth about her 'immaculate conception'. She had taken sperm out of Jonathan's used condom and inseminated herself while he was in the shower!!!!*

As Cambridge University's philosophy don Baroness Onora O'Neill said in the 2002 Reith Lectures, it's all about trust. Picture the perfect, tranquil, domestic family scene in London N11: Kids, suburban house, whipped

# Scheming girlfriend STOLE my sperm to get herself pregnant

**A STUNNED and angry father has made legal history after his devious girlfriend STOLE his sperm and made herself pregnant.**

A court has ordered Jonathan Evans to pay maintenance despite scheming Corinne Tindall confessing she secretly inseminated herself with the contents of a used condom while he was in the shower after making love.

**EXCLUSIVE**
**By ALUN PALMER**

ruling gives a licence to women to use men in any way they see fit. How does this affect the millions of men who have donated sperm? Can they now be sued for maintenance?"

But despite the fact he feels used and

cream, strawberries, and big hugs and kisses from the missus for the good father. Domestic buppie bliss, even though the bank owns everything.

So here I am, the 'new man', married to Ms. Hopelessly In Love, with two point zero kids to keep my mind focused on the job, living happily ever after. Everything is as perfect as perfect can be.

We'll be married later today (yes, the only thing missing from this idyll is the band of gold). This is a result for a man like myself who has done his best to avoid matrimony like it was some form of nasty skin rash. I'm trying to do the right thing, so the last thing I'm expecting is that knock on the door that every man fears — from a kid he never even knew he had fathered.

At the breakfast table, Chardonnay is going through her terrible threes and making us pay with an attitude that we fled the ghetto to escape. My one-year old daughter, Cartier, meanwhile, is trying to make it into the British Olympic sprint team before she's two. Her training consists of seeing whether she can electrocute herself on the wall socket before we manage to rescue her. She's already lost her two bottom teeth for her efforts (I wonder how good she'll be at keeping them when she gets to the teenage years). Throw in the mix a jumble of toys, noise, family photos, guilt and Weetabix (everywhere) and you've got my domestic life in a nutshell. I take it all with a prayer and a bemused smile on my face.

Kids, eh? They drive you crazy, cost you a fortune and they fart in your face. Gotta love 'em, though. How can you not, they are so soft and cuddly. As for ye olde trouble and strife, I've got nothing but mad love for her and I still can't believe that a girl that fine will knowingly go where no woman has gone before (down the aisle) with me.

I wooed her for months with romantic weekends away in country hotels, candle light, roses, chilled bottles of champagne — the works. Played it like Valentino, piled it on thicker than icing on a cake. If there was a Mr Romance competition I would have walked it. From that first night of passion it was clear Sweetie was hooked.

There aren't too many women out there who don't love that old romance thing — a sensual man, flowers and a bottle of Bailey's is hard to resist. No matter how hard the nut, any man with an ounce of intelligence will know that all you gotta get is a better nutcracker. No matter how tough the cookie, a little bit of honey will soften anyone.

I love Sweetie's mind, though. Fortunately, it came wrapped in a nice looking package. We've been through so much together, and we're more in love now than ever, even though I thought it wasn't possible to fall any deeper in love. That's why I'm taking her to the registry office this afternoon, so we can go all legit. I still can't imagine being with, waking up with, or growing old with anyone else. I must be in love because I tolerate all the things I said I wouldn't tolerate before I was with her. I know she's in love because she phones me every couple of hours just to say, "Wha'ppen?" I know we love each other because we share (nearly) everything and spend our lazy Sunday mornings lying in bed listening to *The Archers* omnibus and arguing over how many children to have. Yes, we still argue, but the argument usually gets squashed before it really kicks off.

I feel like I am finally taking control of my life, turning a corner, getting my house in order. I'm becoming more spiritually, emotionally and financially stable.

Like I said, the last thing you want on your wedding day is one of those knocks on the door that completely upsets the applecart. You know the kind — loud, firm, triple rat-a-tat-tat, announcing the realisation of your 'What if...?'

What if you do have a child out there somewhere? What if a child you never knew about turned up on your doorstep, how would you react? What if you don't like

him or her? What if he wants his children to meet the
grandfather who doesn't know their father? It's a whole
new chapter.

Of course, it could never happen. I practiced safe sex
all the time. Almost. And even when I didn't, I always
used contraceptives. Or my partner did. So it's
impossible. I'm 99.999999999999% sure that I won't be
getting that dreaded knock on the door.

I didn't. My doorbell rang instead. You know the type
of ring — long, hard, deliberate. The kind that
announces a visit from the f**k-up fairy.

What if you open the door and the child you never
knew about is standing there? What would you do?
What would YOU do? Shut the door quickly?

Even as I walked those final paces of ignorant bliss
towards the front door, my heart was thumping
inexplicably.

*What if? What if? What if?*

The 'what ifs' were doing my head in, like one big can
of worms — like the worms were out of the can and
eating away inside me, snacking off my intestines. It's
with you every night. Even when you're not thinking
about it. It's there, at the back of your mind, reminding
you: 'What if?' Just when you thought you'd managed to
banish it from your thoughts, someone at a dinner party

asks: "How many kids have you got?" Or you see some programme about absent fathers and you're just about to say you're glad you're not one. Then you start wondering: What if? What if? What if?

I opened the front door to find a half-black (could pass for white if he stayed out of the sun) pickney on the doorstep. Standing there glaring at me.

"Me know you? What do you want? What you staring at?" I snapped.

His eyes flickered with visual aggro. "I'm trying to imagine you with enough personality for my mother to have slept with you."

"You what?"

"Don't act like you weren't expecting me… *dad?*"

Dad? *Aaaaarrrrrrrrrrggggggghhhhhh!*

My consciousness shuts down, my heart starts racing, emotions start stirring and, before I know it, the 'what ifs' become 'what now'. My eyeballs almost pop out with blood rush. My pulse goes *du-dum, du-dum, du-dum!* Sweat pours off my head. I sit bolt upright in bed gasping, unable to get back to sleep as life flashes before my eyes.


It's night time. The night before my wedding. I'm in my jimmies. Sweetie is right there beside me, naked, newly awakened from my midnight screaming.

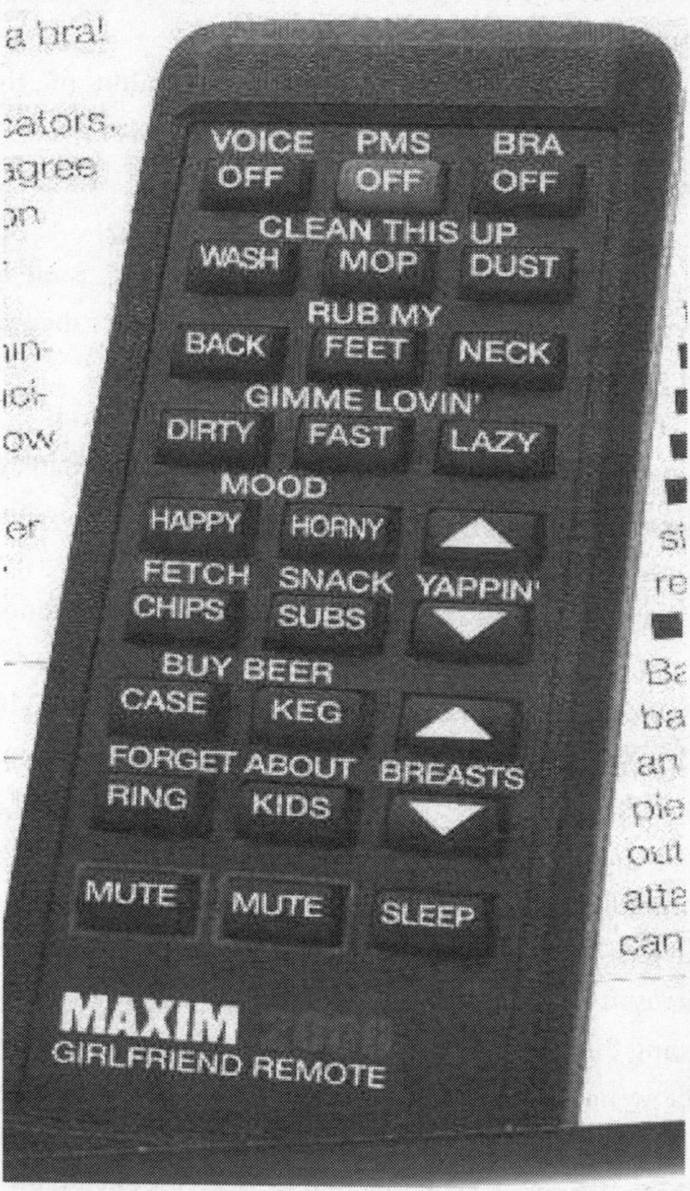
VOICE OFF
PMS OFF
BRA OFF
CLEAN THIS UP
WASH
MOP
DUST
RUB MY
BACK
FEET
NECK
GIMME LOVIN'
DIRTY
FAST
LAZY
MOOD
HAPPY
HORNY
FETCH
CHIPS
SNACK
SUBS
YAPPIN'
BUY BEER
CASE
KEG
FORGET ABOUT
RING
KIDS
BREASTS
MUTE
MUTE
SLEEP
MAXIM
GIRLFRIEND REMOTE

"It's that dream again, isn't it?" she says in an anxious tone.

I nod. Still breathing heavily. My mind on the nightmare, my heart thumping still, like it was going to beat its way out of my chest.

*Whassamatter with me?*

The answer, of course, is probably nothing. Same as everyone else in a similar position. Or maybe it's the fear of the unknown.

I wanted to come clean, tell Sweetie all about it. I figured maybe it might be nice if someone other than my therapist understood what the frigg I was going through. But I've tried before to explain how things were for a man back in his bachelor days. Sweetie just didn't get it.

I took her in my arms and told her that I was all right. That she needn't worry. That it was just a silly dream. But I knew it wasn't.

You see, for years before I met Sweetie, I'd had a string of bad luck with women. I was simply unable to love, so women came and went. It was a case of too many freaks, not enough circuses. I kid you not. I was going through my 'I'm a bachelor with no sign of parole (blow me — no strings attached — here's my number, call or show up naked, bring food) so why bother' phase. I figured I'd be be one of the cool guys with a pum-pum mobile and lots of girls. No main squeeze to frigg up my life. Then came my college phase, my young black and gifted phase, my down and out in London and Paris phase. And now, I'm in the real world. Oh, I always knew that I was eventually going to settle down and get married, but during those phases I wasn't taking any soul mates into consideration. I wasn't looking for a virtuous woman who would be a good wife to me and mother to my children, or who could be my best friend and understand my struggles. I was only interested in dating women who looked better in bridesmaid dresses than in wedding gowns. Then once I had got a taste of some sweet sugar boom-boom, all I was interested in was when to get it, who to get it from and where to do it. Put it this way, if someone gave you a no-limit Barclaycard to go shopping with, would you use it? Hell, yeah!

So what's my point?

I just want to say 'thank you', from the bottom of my heart, to all those women who took care of me during this period. I really mean that. I'd like to dedicate this book to them. Thanks to all the ladies who kept me on my toes (or rather, my knees). Respect due to your lips for the many nights of bliss.

*Rrrrrriiiiiinnnnngg!*

The doorbell sounded. A long, hard, deliberate ring.

"I'll get it," I say to Sweetie in a panic.

"No, you lie down," she says. "You're having a nightmare."

"No, I'll get it," I insist. "You lie down, Sweetie. When I've answered the door I'll come back and give you a back rub. Nice, yeah?"

I managed those twenty steps to the front door like a dead man walking. *What if?* My legs start shaking. *What if?* My heart starts to pump faster and faster. *What if?* Whooooooaah! What the f***'s going on? *What if?* What if? *What if it wasn't a nightmare?* What if the kid really is standing there?

I opened the door and there he was.

"Why d'you have to slam the door on me?" he asked mystified. "Did you really think you could get away with having kids without the responsibility? Times have moved on. Kids are not putting up with their absent fathers' foolishness anymore."

I am stunned.

"D'you know what time it is? It's the middle of the night. Who are you? What do you want? What's your problem? I bet it's really hard to pronounce. I've got problems of my own, you know," I reasoned.

"I'm your son. I want my dad," came the reply I didn't want to hear.

"Excuse me, what was that? It sounds like English, but I can't understand a rhatid word you're saying. I haven't got a son."

So he spelled it out for me. "You see, there are these birds and these bees…"

"I'm not being rude, but it wasn't me. An error's been made. You have to find someone else to blame. I'm not the one. So if you'll excuse me, I've got a wedding to prepare for."

He got dark and said, "You are totally validating my inherent mistrust of black men. You lot just want to have your end away and get away with it. Running from your responsibilities will get you nowhere, I'm here for good. Everywhere you go, I'll be there, watching you. Every breath you take, every move you make…"

"Listen, man, it's been nice meeting you, whoever you are, but don't be reading me my rights. I've done nothing wrong. You've got to go. I'm real sorry, but I'm real high right now and I need to get some juggling done, take care of some business. Na'mean? I've got a family, I haven't got time to blow sunshine up your arse."

"You can't make me leave — *dad*. I came by to see how you were doing. It's time to learn that kids are not for just for Christmas, they're for life."

"Quit calling me 'dad'. You've caused enough chaos, panic and disorder in my life. Your work here is done. Now leave."

In Jamaica, the pretending to a man that a child is his is called 'jacketing'. But don't think that such a practice only happens in JA. Remember, it is estimated that out of every hundred men who are tested to see if they have the same genetic disorders as their child, ten turn out not to be the natural father (with so much bed hopping going on these days I wonder if the one in ten statistic is on the conservative side). It's shocking that the figure is so high, but what is even more of a surprise is that so many men could be so easily deceived.

I know of two guys I'm sure are not natural fathers but who think they are. In one case the child is so obviously not his that it is almost laughable. The child is the spitting image of someone both he and his missus know — there can be no doubt who the father is. Even people in the street who haven't seen his missus in years assume she must have settled down with Mr X because they can recognize him from the child. But the poor dumb husband hasn't got a clue because he would never believe that his wife would go behind his back and sleep with another man. I don't know whether it's blind trust, ego, or the fact that he's just living in denial, but as far as this geezer is concerned this is his child.

Let me make it clear that I haven't got any time for men who father pickney before making a hasty exit, but at the same time I think it's pretty low of a woman to tell a man a child is his when it just isn't.

Well, the writing could be on the wall for those women who try and pull a jacket on a man. A businessman recently won permission from the High Court to sue his former lover for £250,000 after finding out that the twelve-year old boy that he brought up was not his son.

Mr Justice Burnton said in his ruling that women who try to deceive their partners over paternity could be sued for fraud.

Quite bloody right too. I hope that the geezer wins his case and that the law is changed to make it a criminal offence for a woman to falsely claim a man as a father when he isn't. I also hope that the police will start to treat more seriously claims by men that their sperm was stolen by a woman who then used it to make herself pregnant.

Tennis ace Boris Becker has come in for much derision because he has made such a claim against the woman to whom he is paying out child maintenance. Becker claims he never actually had intercourse with the woman (the way Clinton never actually had 'sexual relations' with '*that* woman — Ms Lewinski') and that she must have impregnated herself with his sperm.

Everyone is laughing at the former Wimbledon champ, but how do we know it didn't happen that way? While we're on that subject, did I ever tell you about the time a spaceship full of aliens abducted me and put me to sleep, then left me in the bed of my best mate's girlfriend?

*Rrrrriiiiiiiiinnnnnggg!*

"Mum said you'd be like this," the boy shouted as I opened the door. "Said you were always good for nothing, a playboy, a bulldog. Said you double crossed her. Said you said you loved her, but all you wanted was to get your leg over. You came, you saw, you cocked-up. Left her with a baby to bring up on her own. What kind of man are you?"

*What the f***? Who the f***? Where the f***? WHEN?*

"On a slow boat to Sweden, twenty years ago."

"Sweden? Boat? Yes, I remember. I mean no, you've got it wrong. That's not how it happened. Impossible. I'm 99.999999999999% sure…"

# STAMINA DADDY

*A man is driving down a road. A woman is driving in the opposite direction. As they pass each other, the woman leans out the window and yells, "PIG!"*

*The man immediately leans out his window and yells, "BITCH!"*

*They each continue on their way, and as the man rounds the next bend... he crashes into a huge pig in the middle of the road.*

The new breed of woman plays football and rugby. When she wants a baby, she finds a man and gets pregnant — by 'accident' or design. It happens all the time, even in this age of readily available sperm banks, egg donors, petri dishes and frozen embryos. But twenty years ago I didn't know it could happen to me.

I'm seventeen and I'm horny like a toad. Damn, is it

something in the stars, in the air, in the water? I
suddenly feel so warm. Why is my groin twitching, the
inside of my thigh quivering and my pulse going into
overdrive? Why do I feel that teenage tingle you feel
when you realise that it's not a dream, you really are
about to get laid. Maybe it's the waves, tossing the
Felixstowe-Gothenburg ferry about on the North Sea.
That sort of thing makes some people sick while others
get horny.

I decided to go down to the disco, get drunk and have
some fun. What else was there to do all night long on a
slow boat to Sweden?

**Five minutes later.**

Had a MISERABLE time. It's a Scandinavian thing.
You wouldn't understand.

Look at what they call a disco. I'm glad I didn't have
to pay to get in, I would have been vexed. The music is
rubbish, the dance floor is full of piss artists.

Talking about piss artists, that's what the
Scandinavians love more than anything. Beer for the
Swedes, vodka for the Finns. They drink 'til they're
drunk. I saw one girl throw up, pass out, then piss
herself at the 'disco' bar. Then some guy comes along
with a few too many, slips on her breakfast, falls over
backwards on it and just lies there. Then some unsober
girl dancing some freaky dance on the dance floor gets

thrown in the direction of the drunk-in-puke by a particularly violent dip in the ocean and is thrown face downwards on top of him. Then some bloke who was dancing in just his underpants interprets all this as the woman gagging for it (or so he claimed in court) and dives in on top of her, like it was some love-in — John and Yoko stylee.

It all happened in a matter of seconds. It was mad! I tried chirpsing a coupla beanies in the midst of the mayhem, but they had stuck their noses up their behinds. Talk about material girls, just because I confessed that I drive a VW Beetle with a dent in the side (because some idiot hit my car while it was parked and didn't have the decency to stop) they refused to allow me anywhere near their virginity! One of 'em even had the nerve to say I wasn't worth looking at to spit on! I'm telling you, if women place more importance on what you drive than who you are... screw 'em.

Woe is me, woe is me, woe is me. I chased my tail to get a strong drink. In the mirror behind the barman, I caught my reflection asking, 'How come the magic didn't work? You losing it? Gotta lose some weight, that's what you've got to lose. You're getting too heavy. Look at you. Not fat. Just thick. Look like a bouncer or something. Gotta hit the weights. Get down to the gym and pump.'

No, the chicks didn't exactly come flooding out of the woodwork on the ferry that night, but why should that matter when a man can still have fun by finishing that novel that he's been reading for the last four years (I hope the ending doesn't get all emotional and sentimental).

They should have a strip club on these ferries, to have some real fun. An excellent opportunity to view porn stars you don't get to see every day. And seeing as I've captured the attention of the shipping company, a bottle of cologne in every cabin wouldn't go amiss neither, nor a vase full of rose petals to sprinkle in the bubble bath and on the bunk, so we can dream on them and make love on them. But if you really want travellers to turn their backs on cheap air fares across to Sweden, Norway and Denmark and to make the journey by sea instead, you've got to pack your ferries with sex. Trust me. I love sex like the next man. I love to be in it, around it, in front of it, behind it, on top of it. You get my point? It leads my nose and knows my needs. Right across the North Sea. Sex is just like dope, even if you don't want no more! That reminds me, offering free weed and cocaine is another way to get the crowds travelling by ferry again.

What is it with men and me? Why is it that fellas seeking a little male bonding always seem to gravitate

towards me on the bus, on the tube, the train or even the ferry? There I am staring at myself in the bar mirror and contemplating different ways to make the ferry company rich, when some rugby player type with a thick neck and shoulders that seemed to go on and on in a straight line, comes and orders a large Jack Daniel's.

"Get one for yourself," he tells the barman. "Oh, and anything this gentleman is drinking."

My eyes light up. I thank him. Tell him, "Don't mind if I do."

He props himself up beside me.

"Yeah, I saw you get cussed by those two blondes earlier," he smiles. "Little did you know that they've got their noses up their behinds. Some women are like that, I'm telling you, they don't know any better. It's the truth. I mean, you wonder why they came to the frigging disco if they don't wanna get laid."

I nod. "Y'know wha'I'msayin'."

"Yeah, I know what you're saying, because I was chatting them up earlier. They cussed me too. It's no big loss. Sure, they look gorgeous and, no doubt, have men eating out of the palm of their hands, but they've got the attention span of a two-year old. What are you going to talk about when you're lying in bed with them and you've already heard all the dirt on their girlfriends who wish they had a man like you? What are you going to talk about for the rest of the time?" he asked between clunks of whiskey. "I swear, the longer you're in this game, the more dirt you do, the more you lose faith in the ladies. Then again comes a question: Can ONE woman be your everything? Something is always lacking. Especially in the sex department. They always start off strong, then after a few months or when they feel comfortable (like they have you), they start pleading tiredness and want to palm you off with some measly once/twice a week. Like, you're some old man!"

I nod. "Knowwhatyousayin', man. I was swimming in that same spot in the river a while back. By the way, I'm D."

I stretched out my hand. He shook it warmly. Introduced himself as Bengt. His father was Anglo-Jamaican, his mother a Swede. His surname was Persson, said he had just come out of a particularly bad relationship and didn't need much prompting to go down on the opposite sex (figuratively speaking).

"I guess I'm a perfectionist who seeks the unattainable in a partner — perfection," Bengt continued. "Not perfection as in no flaws, but I need the flaws to be flaws that I can live with. I can't tell you the number of times I've been out with the boys to see if I can get relaxed and get lucky, and I've come across a woman who seemingly has it all, but then you discover that she's a couple of pennies short in one department or another. If you encounter someone that has no class, why should you feel the necessity to stick by them or sink to their level?

"On the few occasions that I've encountered fools and stuck by them or sunk to their depths, I've always regretted it."

I knew where he was coming from with that one, too. Told him so. "One time there was this girl, fell in love with my pistol, begged me to let her make a plaster cast of it. Next thing I know, she's dipped it in gold, silver and brass and it's on sale in Camden Market!"

Bengt found my story amusing. It wasn't meant to be funny.

"You're so sweet," he said, drunkenly, before knocking back another large Jack D's in one gulp. "You know, it's a shame that you're still a virgin…"

"What? *Me?* You've got to be kidding. I was just telling you…"

"Come on, that story sounded sweet, but please, be real, it doesn't prove you're not a virgin. We have all had encounters that we really could and should have gone without."

"Why d'you keep going on about me being a virgin? I just told you… Man, you've been drinking too much of that bad stuff, my mixed-race brotha."

I was giving him a hard time for talking bull about me. Me, a virgin? Yeah, right. I'm seventeen. I've been at it since I was sixteen and a half. I'm practically a veteran.

"I was just teasing you about still being a virgin," Bengt said. "You're so young. Just be careful where you put it about, or the next time you pee it might be like — 'ouch'!"

Maybe I was just imagining it, but did Bengt just pat me on the crotch as he said that? No. Couldn't be. Geezers are not like that with one another.

*Then who?*

Maybe it was the ship dipping in the waves which knocked him in my direction and he just happened to have his hand out at waist height...

I needed to find out for certain.

"Do women really like giving us BJ's better than intercourse? What do you think?" I asked loud and clearly. It was a loaded question. The way he answered it would tell me one way or another.

"Yeah," came the reply. "That's what I've heard. Personally, I like BJs because they stop wrinkles."

What? *What the f-?*

"Yeah, it's great *receiving* a BJ, doh, don't you think?" Still loaded from me.

"You've got to give to receive." He hesitated, before adding, "I'll give you if you'll give me."

No thanks.

"*No* thanks?" It sounded like he had taken my negative response as a personal affront. "There's nothing better to do on this boat for the next twelve hours."

"No thanks."

"No thanks?"

"No thanks."

"*No* thanks?!"

"NO thanks."

"I'll take that as a 'yes' then?" he asked.

"No means 'no'!"

"When men say 'no' they really mean 'maybe, all right then, yes — under duress'."

Suddenly, everything about Bengt seemed to spell G.A.Y — the handlebars moustache, the fingernails painted black, the suit with no wrinkles, his annoying habit of staring at my crotch as we talked. His name even. How could I have missed the obvious signs?

"Let me just set some stuff straight — I don't care about a person's sexual preference, that is your friggin' business. But if you're bi-curious, don't be curious over here."

Bengt knocked back another large Jack D. Still couldn't get his head round the complexity of the word 'no'.

"So does this mean you won't let me suck you off? Go on, be a sport, let me stir your thoughts with my tongue. What else are you going to do, stuck on this ferry with nothing to do?"

Told Bengt once more that I wasn't inna dat. Like I've been hanging round this bar half the evening just waiting for a *man* to sort me out. Yeah, *right*.

To get my mind off all this unwanted attention, I went out on deck with two spliffs and a Heineken, trying hard to remember the last good sex I had had. But either I hadn't had any good sex in a long time, or my memory was fading fast! Silly isn't it, I meet and date and sleep with women, but for what? At the end of the day I can't remember a thing and I still feel, well, alone and lonesome. Damn, but this is some good herb, though… all I need now is a lap dance to prove I'm not gay.

Meanwhile the ocean is going nuts and I'm getting paranoid. This must be what they call a tidal wave. The boat is being tossed like salad with every huge swell. Oh my god, we're all going to die. We're going down like the Titanic… somebody PLEASE help. HELP!!

Damn, this herb's not just good, it's strong, too. Maybe I need to lay off the chronic and *prove* I'm not gay.

Back at the 'disco', the dancers are going wild to Led

Zeppelin. That's when I see her. She was a trip. Doing pirouettes and all kinds of creative dance moves that had nothing to do with the music. It was something to behold.

Our eyes meet across the crowded dance floor. I smile and smile again until, finally, I conquer her with my killer smile. At the same time Bengt comes up from behind and whispers in my ear. "Prove you're not gay. I'se gots ta know."

I get up and walk to the bar to get away from him. She comes up close behind me. She's wearing a pair of white trousers that look electric blue in the disco light, and a dark blouse cut down low in the front. Apparently, she has lost her "testicles" (so you know where her head is at) and she can't see too good without them. Without further ado, she blows a warm vodka breath just below my ear and on the back of my neck, gets me purring.

She's got a tongue like a rattlesnake. I feels sooooooo good when she sticks it in my ear and gently licks. Almost brings me to my knees.

"I would love to feel your goatee between my thighs."

*Oh damn, did she really say that?*

I let out a squeal and say, "I'm in the same boat, girl, I'm in the same boat."

"I love dickie too much," she continues in broken english with a Scandinavian lilt, "especially black dickie."

*Oh damn.* I can hardly contain myself, I'm going to sex heaven. *See, I told you I'm not gay.*

I'm trying to be a gentleman and take it nice and slow, but I can't believe my luck. With twelve more hours of rough North Sea ahead, I'm ready and willing for some adult entertainment to while away the time. It's the best way to ease the sea-sickness.

I turn round to see Bengt leering over in my direction, licking his lips. With hands like an octopus, I pull the gal towards me and stick two fingers up at Bengt behind her back.

"Take me drunk, I'm home," she gasps, ripping my shirt open.

So I took her down below for some special treatment.
*But you swore you would never do a one night stand.*

Yeah, right, do men who don't do that still exist?
*But, but, but…*

Damn, now see what you've done — just thinking about it — I need to go and take a shower.

Down in my cabin, she didn't wait for me to take off my trousers, but ripped them off herself. Then she ripped her clothes off and turned round for me to admire the 'ABBA' tattoo on her batty.

"Are you ready?" she growls. "It's going to be a long

night. I hope you have some skillz."

With that she reaches down into that hairy jungle of mine, digging her fingernails deep into the flesh on the inside of my thighs, grabs it where it matters and guides it in — wiggling and jiggling and wiggling and jiggling inch after inch after inch after… Then that first moan and the look of pleasure in her eyes. Her body shakes like she's having a seizure. I must be doing something right. That's what it's all about, the pleasure in pleasing.

"Give it to me… harder," she panted. "Do it from the back — yah, that's my fave. Dawgy style. What angle do you want my legs at — 45, 90, 180?"

Her beefy thighs damn near wear me out with some hair-pulling, back-scratching, bum-slapping, slamming-me-up-against-the-wall-and-waking-the-neighbours-up, calling-me-names kinda sex. Slow. Fast. Slow. Fast. More and more urgent. Switch positions. Fast. Slow. Fast. Slow.

I'm exhausted, shattered, shagged, floating in a twisted mass of legs and arms and lips and tongues, savouring the moment. My hips hurt! My legs hurt! My abs hurt! I need a massage!! I almost died when it came time for climax. I think she had to administer C.P.R. because my heart stopped.

But she's just getting warm.

"Åååå! No, once is not enough," she screams.

"Herregud! Don't stop! Jävla förbannad skitstövel. Knulla mig, sade jag. Ja — ja, ja, ja! Jo — jo, jo, jo, precis så... visst, det känns så jävla bra. Heja Sverige! Och nu kommer jag, nu kommer Pippi Långstrump, tjula hopp, tjula hej, tjula hopp san sa! Ja, ja visst, svarta gör det bättre. Ja visst ja."

Many women are happy to say, 'It doesn't matter if I don't climax'. This woman wasn't having any of that. It did matter. Big Time. And she wanted to come — over and over and over again.

"You didn't just come once, you came twice," I point out.

"Don't stop," she screams, as I shift down a gear or two. "Set my crotches on fire. Even if it spoils my eyesight. I want to climb the walls like Spiderman, until my toes touch the ceiling."

I tried my best to comply with some serious lovemaking — bobbing and weaving like a heavyweight champ — until I was too bruised to carry on. She, meanwhile, was taking little bites out of my chest, the back of my neck, my shoulder, several harsh bites along my spine, while massaging my scalp with her fingernails.

We were at it all night. Literally. It hurt so good that I forgot my own name and didn't even ask for hers. She pulled me 69 different ways, only pausing once to take a leak. F'real. She was like, "Stay tuned, I will return after this brief commercial break." On her return she continued where she left off.

BANG! BANG! BANG! BANG!

*Damn, this is a ferry, not a plantation. Talk about 'do you remember the days of slavery...'*

It was lust, pure and simple.

I must have passed out on the job, because the next thing I know it's morning and she's waking me up with the oral thing. "Making up for being so greedy last night," she grins, flashing an uneven set of yellow teeth.

Have you ever been with someone and then when you look at them afterwards you feel physically sick? I look at her and get nauseous. Maybe the yucky feeling I have in my stomach is less to do with her and more to do with the disappointment in myself. Like, 'How could I have been with such a promiscuous woman?' Or am I the slag here?

"Of course I'll call you when I get to Stockholm," I say, knowing it's entirely out of the question.

I wish I had kept her number, though, instead of tossing it overboard.

# TAKING THE KISS

*Mark and Roberta Griswold from Michigan in the USA puckered up their lips and kissed continuously for a record twenty-nine hours during a kissing contest in New York in March 1998. Throughout the attempt the couple remained standing without rest breaks.*

*The achievement of the Griswolds is of particular relevance because July 6th has been declared National Kissing Day by a toothpaste manufacturer. Denplan is trying to encourage the rather reserved Brits to use the day as a good reason to give their partner a proper snog.*

*Apparently, many of us are rather reluctant to give our loved one a kiss. Men in particular would rather shake their girlfriend's hand than join lips. It may have something to do with the fact that many mouths smell about as fresh as a hamster's cage. So, to help the day along and overcome any fears about dodgy breath, Denplan is promoting its Beverley*

*Hills formula anti-stain whitening mouth-rinse which comes
with a free tongue scraper.*

*(The plastic scraper is there to aid the removal of bacteria
from the back of the tongue. How nice. I think I'll stick to a
firm handshake!)*


Meanwhile, back to my wedding day.

"Wakey, wakey!"

We were woken early for the big day. Already
downstairs, a military operation was underway as
various women rushed to get up all the ivy and the fancy
decorations. The marquee was already standing in the
garden and the sunlight was exploding on its white
canvas. I kissed my bride-to-be, who was looking
fabulous. "How ya feeling, hon?" I asked.

"I had a mad crazy dream last night that doesn't
make sense," she replied.

"*You?* Dream?"

"Men aren't the only ones that can have dreams,
right?"

"So what was this dream, darling?"

"More a nightmare than a dream. We are at about to
be pronounced man and wife... But there are all these
angry women... pushing prams... and when the pastor
gets to the point where he asks 'Is there anyone present
who knows of any reason why D and Sweetie should not

be joined in holy matrimony?' all these babies jump out of the prams and start calling you 'dad'! You did say that you haven't got any other kids out there, didn't you…?"

The whole marriage thing was Sweetie's idea, of course. I'm not saying I was reluctant, I was just nervous. I waited years for the right woman to finally come along and I wanted to make sure I was doing the right thing. I was getting tired of the running around and wanted to settle down, but I didn't want to change. Despite Sweetie's assurances to the contrary, I felt sure marriage was going to totally change me. It had already put a stop to me using the world as my urinal, even before our wedding day. The fellas now write their names in the snow without me.

So before I agreed to the nuptials, I got her to sign my man's manifesto:

1. I shall endeavour to be the man of your dreams, as long as you promise not to dream of a man that's not me.

2. I will be the perfect father. But when the going gets tough and our love wilts, you promise not to use the children against me.

3. I will really try to be faithful. But if I fail, you agree that you'll try to

see it as a weakness of the flesh and won't take it personal.

4. There will always be a 'young lad' inside me bursting to be 'free'. So let me grow old slowly.

5. I will worship and cherish you, but when 'the lads' are around, let me pretend that I wear the trousers.

6. I won't lie to you. Unless I have to.

She read it and grunted an acknowledgment.

Once it was signed, all we had to agree on was how much the whole thing was going to cost.

*"HOW MUCH??????!!!!!!!"*

"Weddings are expensive, D, whichever way you look at it. Both our families are kinda big. We've got to invite all those West African uncles and aunts of yours that aren't really blood and what not. So we've got to discuss everything. To accommodate everybody we need to hire one of the ballrooms at the Dorchester Hotel on Park Lane, where we will also have a suite reserved for that night and the day after. I want a nice, simple designer wedding dress, preferably the Chanel one I saw with the buttons down the back, and a simple veil. I've got to get my hair braided into a ball, so I'll have to crown my head with a diamond tiara. I want one flower girl, seven bridesmaids, two maids of honour, and a cute toddler as the ring bearer. Then there's the wreaths of little white flowers, they cost money too. I want to walk down the aisle to beautiful music played by a live chamber orchestra, not a recording of that traditional wedding march. Rather than say my vows, I'd rather sing them to you. That's free. But everything else is going to cost."

I told her, if she wanted a wedding like that then she needed to find someone else to marry 'cause I'm not going broke over something that will last hours at the most. "There are lots of men out there who are willing to rob a bank to get married. Might not be the type of husband you had in mind, but at least you will get the vows."

Of course, I was only kidding. F'real doh, if more women admitted that the reason they wanted to get married was to have a big wedding, I bet there would be fewer divorces happening out there. Men just don't know what they're letting themselves in for. Someone should start a business and call it 'Weddings without marriages'. I bet they'd do a roaring trade.

"Okay, Sweetie, I'll go all out on the ring and I'll even chuck in a fairy tale honeymoon, but the wedding's got to be small and intimate and romantic — for our blood

relatives and closest friends. We'll have the reception at home." And I told the pastor, "I don't want a sermon, thank you. Short and sweet and cheap run t'ings. Seen?"

He said simply, "Congrats on finding your queen. Treat her as such. I envy you."

It was a typical buppie wedding. It started an hour after the time on the invites. The photographer took 955,603 pictures and none of them came out. The best man wore sunglasses and answered his mobile during the ceremony and, in true best man tradition, got so drunk that he decided to let the rum do the talking on his behalf when he couldn't find his prepared speech.

"My lords, ladies and gentlemen... Love may be blind, but marriage is the real eye-opener."

He looked around the room with a puzzled expression, unable to recognize any faces and wondering whether he might be in the wrong place, but continued anyway.

"As I was saying my lords, ladies and gentlemen, I come not to diss my good spar who got married today (one day he'll look back on today and have a good laugh), but to praise him. Thank God for common sense is what I say. Because every man needs a woman to wake up to.

"I'm here to praise the bride, too. Not only because

she loves him, but because she so profoundly identifies with the genetic inheritance that made him the human being that he is.

"But to the groom, D, you need to redirect your focus, mate. Compliment her, respect her, honour her, cuddle her, kiss and caress her, love her, tease her, comfort her, protect her, wine and dine her, listen to her, care for her, stand by her, support her, admire her, go to the ends of the Earth for her. I know we fellas like to say 'what's the use of the truth if you can't tell a lie', but never, never ever lie to her or hide the truth from her. Unless you REALLY have to.

"Don't think just cause you've now got someone who can fix up some drinks and sandwiches for you and your spars when we're watching the big match on cable round at your yard, that you can just ease up. You're going to need to focus more than ever on bringing home the corn so you can buy your beautiful wife all the nicer things of life. You need to start looking for a new job, mate, because the one you've got is not paying enough for a newlywed. You have to start sending out your CV soon. Maybe start on Monday, yeah? Find a gig that pays serious loot.

"Unlike you, I am still able to continue running around with lots of different women. It's a shame though. I'd trade it all in for one true soul mate like you've got. And when that seven year itch comes around and you feel like trading it all in for my lifestyle, just consider what your daughters would think if you had an affair and got caught.

"To the beautiful bride, Sweetie, a few words of advice: Men get married because it makes their life better. Having hot meals, clean sheets, and a well stocked fridge helps to make life just that little bit better. On average married men live longer than single men. Why do you think that's so? Because of the good works of their dear wives, that's why.

"Now you're married, never let your husband's mind wander — it's too little to be out alone. Try not to think about breaking up. Love is powerful, but if it's not on fire, keep stoking. If he asks 'what sort of books you're interested in', tell him cheque books. Remember, 'a sense of humour' does not mean that you tell him jokes, it means that you laugh at his. And never ever imagine you can change a man, unless he's in a nappy."

Right about this point I started feeling bad again. I was doing fine until the bit about never lying or hiding the truth from my wife. Then I started wondering… Have I REALLY got another kid out there? Did she just use me to get pregnant on the ferry? It seems like every time I start thinking about it, I start hurting inside and hoping this was all one terrible dream.

But it wasn't.

*Riiiiiiiiiiiing!*

"Yo, D," my best man called out, "there's some bloke on the doorstep, says he's looking for his dad."

I jumped up, left my new wife at the head table, rushed to the front door.

There he was. Just standing there. If looks could kill he would be deadly at 400 yards away.

"So what happened after you had your end away on the ferry?" he growled. "How come you ended up abandoning your child?"

What happened twenty years ago? Basically, she had kept my number and called me up a few weeks after our session on the ferry.

"God morgon," her voice screeched down the line. "How are you? Glad you made it back safe and sound. I just called to say 'hej'. How come you don't call? Where were you last night...?"

*Gotta think of a good excuse to get off the phone. Hmmmm...*

We exchanged pleasantries. Then I told her I was busy. Had things to do and people to chat to, "If ya catch my drift." I had already moved on and thought she had too.

How wrong I was.

She kept talking. Chatting rubbish about how she would like some "nekkid & half-nekkid" pics of me for her to remember my by and whether I'd like some of her.

I had seen enough of her nakedness to last me a lifetime. But I didn't say that. I'm just too nice, that's my biggest flaw. How do you tell someone who's crazy about you that you aren't in love with them, without make a bad situation worse? I decided to let her down easy. I told her to find herself a man, have some sex.

"I was out having some fun last night. That's why I didn't call you. I'm in a long distance relationship," I announced down the phone line. "My woman is thousands of miles away and it's real hard. She's out of the country and I'm hating it. 'Cause we're mad about each other. But she's supposed to be back in a couple of weeks."

She ignored what I said in that way she had of pretending that the last couple of minutes never really happened. "Oh, I can't even drop by to say 'hej'?" I was like "I'm getting ready for college. I have to take care of some business this morning."

"Oh, you can't speak?" she asked. "I just wanted to tell you that sleeping with you was the best mistake of my life."

"What?" I didn't have a clue.

"I have just found out that I am NOT NOT NOT NOT NOT NOT pregnant."

I couldn't believe she just said that. The very mention of the word 'pregnant' just frigging killed my mood. Even though I knew that she couldn't have been referring to our brief encounter, I had misgivings about it.

"NOT NOT NOT NOT NOT NOT pregnant. What does that mean?" I ask.

"Let me break it down for you — I'm pregnant. Guess who the father is?"

I'm getting angry now. I knew it was a wind-up. Had to be. She was wasting my time. I wasn't going to fight it though, I just decided to let her have it her way if she wanted it.

"But how?"

"How? The usual way — a stray sperm in the semen met up with an egg, and the result…"

"But you said you were protected, remember?" *Swore she was.* "That egg shouldn't have been there in the first place."

"I don't remember a thing. I was drunk the whole time I was on that ferry. Under the influence of vodka and coke. I'm not responsible for my actions."

"You know, you're scaring me a little here. This is a wind-up isn't it? You are going to crawl back to your bed and have a good laugh about how you had me going, aren't you?"

Nothing but silence replied.

"Don't go busting a man out like this," I pleaded. "It's not cricket to get pregnant without discussing it. What about what I want?"

"It's nothing to do with you. I'm going to have this baby. I don't want to see you and, no, I don't want you to drop by. No, no, no. You're the father, but you'll have nothing to do with the baby. You will never hear from me again. I'm going overseas tonight, you will never see me again. I'm not calling you back."

"Wait, hold on, I'm sorry... don't go, don't hang up angry... please, gimme your number, let me call you back. Please don't hang up..."

*Click.*

"...Where the hell are you? Don't make me have to go on a search or something... everything is cool. I'm sorry for that outburst... I want to be a father to my child... I swear!"

I lost my voice yelling and screaming at the dialtone.

# RACE RELATIONS

*A young white woman in the maternity ward just prior to labour is asked by the midwife if she would like her husband to be present at the birth.*

I'm afraid I don't have a husband" she replies.

"Okay. Do you have a boyfriend?" asks the Midwife.

"No, no boyfriend either."

"Do you have a partner then?"

"No, I'm unattached, I'll be having my baby on my own."

*After the birth the midwife again speaks to the young woman.* "You have a healthy bouncing baby girl. I can see from her colour that her father is black. Is that correct?"

"Well," replies the girl. "I was very down on my luck, with no money and nowhere to live, and so I accepted a job in a porno movie. The lead man happened to be black."

"Oh, I'm very sorry," says the midwife, "that's really none of my business and I'm sorry that I have to ask you these awkward questions but I should also tell you that the baby has blonde hair."

"Well yes," the girl again replies, "you see I desperately needed the money and there was this Swedish guy also involved in the movie, what else could I do?"

"Oh, I'm sorry," the midwife repeats, "that's really none of my business and I hate to pry further but your baby has slanted eyes."

"Well yes," continues the girl, "I was hard up and there was a Chinese man also in the movie. I had no choice."

At this, the midwife again apologises collects the baby and presents her to the girl, who immediately proceeds to give baby a slap on the butt. The baby starts crying and the mother exclaims, "Well thank god for that!"

"What do you mean?" says the midwife, shocked.

"Well," says the girl extremely relieved, "I had this horrible feeling that it was going to bark."


My man down the barber reckons that when he and his missus got hitched they were at it for three days non-stop and that even now he plays the bedroom bully for hours with her every night of the week. Yeah right. I believe that like I believe a green pig called Johnny will fly pass my window tomorrow being pursued by a UFO.

What is it with guys? Every Harry, Tom and their tool reckons they are the Terminator — can't be stopped.

Sorry hombre, but I'm not buying it! I want sex just as much as the next twisted bloke, but I sure as hell can't find the time to be doing it every night of the week when I've got kids and a mortgage to be worrying about.

But still the guys will be bigging it up, and who can say they're telling porkies?

Well, the latest research from the States sheds new light on what the 'average' is likely to be. Professor John Robinson of Maryland University has just published the findings of his report into the sexual activity of Yanks.

His conclusions were that only one in twenty Americans got it going on three or more times a week. His co-researcher, Geoffrey Godbey says "Americans like to come on like they're hot stuff but really we are pathetic wimps who can't even get it up. We're losers in the bedroom. Why, I'm ashamed to admit to being an American."

Actually, I lied. Mr Godbey didn't say that, but in an ideal world he would have. The ideal world where I could perform brain transplants and Naomi Campbell was a lecturer in quantum physics. Anyway, back to earth. What Mr Godbey actually said was, "Americans have sex about once a week, much less often than many think."

Not surprisingly the researchers found that married

couples have more sex than single folk because a partner is readily available. The study found that those who work 60 hours a week or more have sex about 66 times a year; while those who work 30-39 hours a week actually do it less often at around 54 times a year. Interestingly, 15 per cent of adults engage in half of all the sexual activity in the U.S. As Churchill said, "Never has so much been done to so many by so few."

I would have thought that if in America (the land of excess, where everything is bigger and better), they were doing it only once a week, then us Brits are likely to be faring even worse. Who knows how infrequently we might be doing it?

Of course everyone is going to say they are among the 5% who do it more than three times a week. But people lie about everything. To any of the average guys out there who are concerned that they are not doing it enough I would say rest yuhself, you are perfectly normal.

You should only become concerned if you and your missus are asked to help in a survey similar to the Yank one. If you tick the box which says you have sex 'once a week' and she ticks the one marked 'five to ten' then, my friend, you had better start worrying.

All that is by way of saying our wedding night at an exclusive hotel for newlyweds (where there was nothing but humping going on in all the other rooms ) was a sedate affair. "I know we've been through a lot together Sweetie, but — tonite is the nite — let's leave our troubles behind. We'll forget everything and have great sex," I was hoping.

We checked in way after midnight.

"You and the lady enjoy yourselves," said the bell boy with a knowing wink as I slipped him a large bill. "And if you need any Viagra or strong herb to see you through the night, I know where you can get the best."

I told him that wouldn't be necessary, but if it became necessary I knew where to find him.

The room was massive. Executive Honeymoon suite. The first thing we did was strip and take a bubble bath together in the jacuzzi while sipping on chilled Bollinger. It was heaven. But why was it so hard to get my swerve on? I just couldn't figure out.

Sweetie refilled her champagne glass and then started climbing out of the jacuzzi.

"It's been such a long day," she yawned. "I think I'm ready for bed."

"Sure bloody," I agreed. "I'm about ready too."

Everything was scripted — the music, the moves. I'd been thinking about this for weeks now. Music: Sade, the Modern Jazz Quartet, Jill Scott, Miles Davis, Verdi.

Moves: Casanova, Snoop Doggy Dogg.

How come I wasn't down with the programme? Was it first night nerves, exhaustion? My body was falling apart. My knees hurt, shoulder hurt, neck stiff. I was frigged up and still on edge.

Sweetie fell asleep first. But if I thought I was also going to sleep off the day, then I had another thing coming.

That knock on the door again. This time louder. Firmer. More determined. I jumped out of bed and went to open. Guess who?

"What the hell are you talking about: 'life without knowledge is death in disguise'? You're really starting to get on my nerves. You know that? How the hell did you find me?" I took a towel and wiped the sweat off my face. I had to keep my voice down because Sweetie is a light sleeper. "What do you want?!! I've told you what happened. I'm innocent. That should be enough."

I wish I hadn't answered the door.

"Oh, I'm so sorry to barge in on you, but I was missing you already and I had to come and see your beautiful face again. After a lifetime of not knowing my father, I can hardly wait to spend more time with you. Can't we just talk it out? Do you even want to? If it doesn't work out, at least you tried."

My better judgement was to let sleeping dogs lie and

let the world turn, but of course I said "Okay." It's hard to say 'no' to your flesh and blood.

"But this is my wedding night," I whispered, mindful of my new bride lying in bed inside the suite. Fortunately, still asleep. I closed the door gently and, wearing only a pair of boxers, joined my 'son' out in the hotel corridor.

"If you knew what it was like to grow up never knowing your father, you wouldn't stand there and tell me it was your wedding night. This is all your fault. If you knew how I've grown angrier with every day... If you knew the murder on my mind. You can't imagine the havoc you've caused in other people's lives just because you couldn't exercise more self-control on that ferry all those years ago. I don't know if I will ever be able to let go of the hurt and that last bit of anger that's held me back all these years. So... tell me something interesting about yourself. I feel like I'm doing all the talking. It's your turn. Tell me something interesting. Where would you like to travel? Do you like warm or cold weather? What's your favourite fruit?"

One minute he was ready to kill somebody and the next minute he had tears streaming down his face. All of that stirred up stuff inside me that I thought I had in check. I felt I owed it to him to see if I had any feelings for him.I thought that in spite of everything I might be overcome by feelings of fatherhood. I hoped I would. But I didn't feel anything at all. It felt like he was a complete stranger. I knew there and then that there was no way we could ever have a proper father and son reunion. It hurts even more to realise this. After all, his was a life I helped create and the fact that I wasn't there for those moments while he was growing up really hurts.

I kept gawking. Something just didn't feel right. My mind's telling me 'no', but my body's telling me 'yeah'. Why can't we go back in time and right our wrongs? Oh well, the best thing for us is to be civil to one another.

"Listen," I said sympathetically, "I'd like to say come on in and chill for as long as you like — throw down whatever's on your mind. But I can't. My bride's inside... asleep. She doesn't know about you... yet."

"Let me just ask you one thing, if you didn't want a child, why didn't you keep your tool in your trousers? Why didn't you use a condom?"

"I totally agree with you. It's all about trust. The fact of the matter is that people slip up..."

"Slip up? *Slip up?* For years, I didn't have a father. You didn't contribute to my life. Some slip up? She told you years ago, even before I was born. You could at least have come looking."

"But I never knew for certain."

"How can you not know for certain how many kids you've got?"

That's the thing isn't it? No man can ever really know. Only a woman knows for sure.

"Easy cum easy go, eh?," he continued. "You could not resist the temptation. That's nothing to be proud of. Those few minutes of fun got someone pregnant. Whether you like it or not you got a kid out of it. So now what are you going to do? Are you going to take care of your business or not? Or are you going to be one of those 'wotless baby fathers' that I've heard so much about?"

I'm not like that. Really I'm not. It's just that this thing has mashed me up. Believe me, I can do without the headaches that come with the prodigal son.

I know a number of adoptees who had perfectly good and loving upbringings, who are haunted by the thought that their biological parents didn't want them. Why do the ones who find out their mothers really loved them, but were made to give them up, feel so moved and reassured? What difference could it possibly make?

There was a recent television programme about sperm-donor children. Some of them were grown-up, even middle-aged. Yet all felt a fierce connection to their biological fathers, a desire to know that the donation wasn't just made for financial reasons. And some are quite badly damaged by the lack of the man who had 'made them'.

There's a primitive side of us that knows we are half mother and half father, and when one of them is absent, unavailable, hostile or denied, there is often an equally primitive sense in children that there is something hidden or unacceptable about half of their inherent nature. It's not easily put right by words and reassurance. Other men or women can provide role models, but they don't speak to the basic 'Who-am-I?' question which surfaces during adolescence and which, for some people, goes on throughout their lives. We profoundly identify with the genetic inheritance that made us the human beings that we are.

# IF YOU AIN'T GOT LOVE

*Americans Peter Wallis and Kellie Smith met at work, fell in love, shared an apartment. Then Wallis sued Smith for becoming pregnant against his will, accusing her of 'intentionally acquiring and misusing' his semen when they had sexual intercourse.*

*Wallis claimed that Smith promised to take birth control pills, and that amounted to a contract, but that then she quit without telling him, essentially forcing him into a role he did not choose: fatherhood.*

*Smith said she became pregnant accidentally while on the pill. She argued that she could not have stolen Wallis's sperm because he "surrendered any right of possession to his semen when he transferred it during voluntary sexual intercourse." "It should be considered a 'gift'," she said.*

Call it the facts of fatherhood — the rewards and curses

of being a man — but it is women who are in complete control of the pricks of this world. And, let's face it, it's so hard to find a one-prick woman these days.

Men just never know for sure. There are all kinds of freaks out there. If you're a man, you have to live with the fact that you've released billions of sperms into the wilderness (up to 400 million per your average slam). That could have resulted in hundreds of kids, thousands even (so far as I am aware the record number of kids for a man was 888 by the old emperor of Morocco).

For all you know, during that reckless period you call 'youth', you fathered a whole gang of kids that you know nothing about. You never know, those kids could be going through their reckless period right now and because they don't all have the same surname... You get the picture — you could be a grandfather right now, both a paternal *and* maternal grandparent to the same child, without even knowing it. You never know.

You never know who is regarding your sperm. It could be some woman you've never ever slept with, let alone one you've set eyes on and liked her smile and her style and two-twos, before you could say 'con-dom', you've been bangin' away like a couple of sausages in a frying pan. It could even be a woman you know well — the girl next door, that good friend of the family, or the dreaded ex. If she decides to liberate your sperm, there's

# The sperm that turned

If a woman gets pregnant by a man without his prior consent, is she secretly stealing his seed? **Raekha Prasad** reports

I t is accepted practice when gathering honey to dodge the sting of the bee. So, too, women have chosen to take the seminal fluid and ditch the man. For a woman wanting a child who isn't looking for or can't find father material, variations on the turkey baster and one-night stand offer a solution. But growing calls for the rights of fathers have stirred a backlash: the sperm is starting to turn.

So Kellie Smith is finding as she faces Peter Wallis in a courtroom in Albuquerque, New Mexico. Wallis has accused Smith of stealing his sperm. He claims that she promised to take the Pill, but deliberately stopped in order to have a baby — making him a father without his knowledge or consent. Smith's lawyer argues that she could not have "stolen" Wallis's sperm because he "surrendered any right of possession ... when he transferred it ... during voluntary sexual intercourse".

daughter, Marie, now four, during a brief affair. She decided not to use contraception in the hope that she would become pregnant. "I didn't consider it a deceitful act," she says. "He never asked me if I was using the Pill. Like many men, I suspect he presumed." The affair ended before she knew she was pregnant; she has had no contact with Marie's father since. "He has no redress as far as I'm concerned. He didn't wear a condom or take measures to stop the spill."

Peter Wallis claims that Kellie Smith is guilty of "intentionally acquiring and misusing" his sperm. He is seeking unspecified damages to reimburse him for the "economic injury" of helping to support the child over the next 18 years, even though Smith has not asked for child support.

he donation of sperm is now within the law. But to avoid any question of

not a damn thing you can do about it.

When I try and reason with some women about this, they'll be like, "Excuse me, you dummy — blaming mothers for failing to use birth control — why didn't you use a johnnie?" Fellas on the other hand KNOW where I'm coming from. They'll be like, "Blowjobs, mate. That's the solution. Blowjobs — the Irish contraceptive. It's foolproof. Even the Pope approves."

Sure, that might seem like where the smart money's at. But blowjobs don't come cheap. Ask Boris Becker. He found out to his cost that a blowjob can result in a ginger-haired kid nine months later. When I remind fellas about Boris they'll be like, "Phew, thanks for pulling my coat on that, bro'. Shame, doh, cause I love my morning fellatio. I won't even lie to you." But when I point out to women that a blowjob can't protect a man when a sperm bandit's about, some women just refuse to accept the fact. I've come to the conclusion that there are women out there who'd rather see a man slam his genitals in a van door than accept that the sisterhood has rogue elements. They would sooner do the funky chicken across a minefield than agree with men on this one.

A lot of women are afraid to condemn their own for fear of being seen as traitors. Lest the accusing finger of their fellow woman should point at them: "It's all right for her, she's already had a child." But the reality is out there staring them in the face every day.

SPERM BANDITS!

"D! D!! Get up! Wake up, sleepyhead, it's ten-thirty in the morning."

I wake in a cold sweat. Still in the honeymoon suite. "Ten thirty!"

Sweetie was sitting cross-legged on the bed beside me.

"You've been having nightmares. You've kept me up all night."

I come to my senses slowly, trying to distinguish dream from reality.

"That's the third time this week?" Sweetie continues, a worried expression on her face. "What's going on, D? What's this dream all about? Why do you keep having it? Are you keeping something from me? Do you have anything you need to say to me?"

I panic. I knew I had to tell her, if only to get it off my chest. My problems are my problems, that's the way it's always been. I have my own way of dealing with things and trying to get through the little dips of life. That's just the way I am. But this is different.

"Come on, D, hurry up. If you've got something to

say, say it, because we're running late. We've got a flight to catch, remember?"

Our honeymoon! I want to tell her now, I've got to tell her now... but on the other hand we've saved up for this honeymoon for ages, we've both looked forward to it. I just don't know how she would take it if I told her. It could ruin everything. Even if it didn't, I couldn't let her go off on honeymoon with this on her mind. I might as well wait until we get back home, not to spoil her trip. I've just got to hope those damn nightmares don't keep coming back.

I know (trust me, I KNOW), I should have told Sweetie all about it ages ago. But I honestly didn't know, not for sure, that I was a father. I never had any evidence of it. I mean, I never saw the woman again. She knew how to get in touch with me for years after, and she didn't. I had no way of contacting her. How could I have been sure that it wasn't a wind-up? Then when the kid turned up at the door... I couldn't give my wife news like that on our wedding day, could I?

# EXCUSES

"A man takes the day off work and decides to go out golfing. He is on the second hole when he notices a frog sitting next to the green. He thinks nothing of it and is about to shoot when he hears, 'Ribbit, 9 iron.'

"The man looks around and doesn't see anyone. Again, he hears, 'Ribbit, 9 iron.'

"He looks at the frog and decides to prove it wrong. He swaps his club for a 9 iron.

"Boom!

"He hits it 10 inches from the cup. He is shocked. He says to the frog, 'Wow, that's amazing. You must be a lucky frog, eh?'

"The frog replies, 'Ribbit, lucky frog.'

"The man decides to take the frog with him to the next hole. 'What do you think frog?' the man asks. 'Ribbit, 3 wood.'

"The guy takes out a 3 wood and — Boom! — hole in one.

*The man is befuddled and doesn't know what to say. By the end of the day, the man had played the best game of golf in his life. He asks the frog, 'OK where to next?'*

*"The frog replies, 'Ribbit, Las Vegas.' They go to Las Vegas and the guy says, 'OK frog, now what?' The frog says, 'Ribbit, Roulette.' Upon approaching the roulette table, the man asks, 'What do you think I should bet?' The frog replies, 'Ribbit, $3,000, black 6.' Now, this is a million-to-one shot to win, but after the golf game the man figures what the heck. Boom! Tons of cash comes sliding back across the table.*

*"The man takes his winnings and books the best room in the hotel. He sits the frog down on the bed and says, 'Frog, you've won me all this money and I am forever grateful. How can I repay you.'*

*"The frog replies, 'Ribbit, kiss me.' He figures why not, since after all the frog did for him, he deserves it. With a kiss, the frog turns into a gorgeous 15-year-old girl.*

*"And that, your honour, is how the girl ended up in my room. So help me God or my name is not William Jefferson Clinton."*

What better honeymoon could there be than a week's all-inclusive stay at the Half Moon in Montego Bay?

When the Air Jamaica flight landed at the airport some of the older passengers clapped and cried "Praise God!"

The customs man let Sweetie pass through, no problem, then noticed me in my pale blue summer suit and snakeskin shoes, and pulled me over.

"Hey man," he said, "you're looking real sharp. Where did you get that suit?"

"I have a good tailor in London."

"Yeah? You must take me to him. That's a real sharp outfit. Now, if you wouldn't mind, step into my office."

He decided to question me for about fifteen minutes. Searched me too, like a common criminal.

"One wallet and one pair of shoes and only one suitcase for a week's vacation? My suspicions are aroused. I can keep you here all night on suspicion… but that is a sharp suit though."

I've never been so embarrassed. I vented my frustration.

"Kiss me neck, now that you mention it, that did sound like a threat. Would you like one?" he burps, holding up a packet of ciggies.

"No thanks. I don't smoke."

"Oh… you don't?"

"Well… no."

"I bet you mean you don't smoke cigarettes."

"Well, if you want to put it that way, I don't smoke cigarettes," I replied impatiently. I was in a hurry to get out of the airport and commence my honeymoon. "Listen, I've done nothing wrong. I'd like to go now if you've finished with me. It's getting late."

"Oh, all right then, but how about a little smoke before you go? Keep it to yourself, this is strickly between me and you. If word gets out I'm done for. I've got some good stuff…"

I thanked him for the offer but declined. "I'm not stupid, I know a set-up when I see one."

"No, really, I've got some top grade stuff," he winked. "That's what you came to Jamaica for isn't it? We've got lovely weed and lovely weather. In that order. Or maybe you just need to get laid? Either way, I'm your man. Here's my card."

He finally let me go. "Enjoy your stay in JA," he waved as Sweetie and I jumped into a taxi.

We spent most of the next five days in bed at our private chalet at the Half Moon. Sweetie got her groove back, I got my swerve on, it was like we were in love for the first time all over again. Fantastic. Can life get any better than this? Yet lawd, I hope so.

We only left the hotel compound once, to go to a top class restaurant on our 'off night'. Even then we spent the whole time holding hands and gazing in each other's eyes, while a belly dancer called Madame Climax entertained in the background.

"You look tired, darling," Sweetie looked concerned. "You look like you could do with a strong black coffee with lots of sugar."

It wasn't a coffee I needed, it was a jar full of multi vitamins and a jug of water.

"Last night was the bomb," I smiled. "And the night before… and the night before that, too."

We decided to give it a rest when we got back to the hotel that night. We both preferred to sit and talk. We had been doing a lot of talking in between the bedsheets anyway. I lay on top of the sheets in my briefs, thinking. I knew I had to come up with a good excuse.

I don't know if it's a consequence of having to develop survival instincts out on the street, but your average man is only beaten by government ministers when it comes to the use of imagination in the excuse department. It doesn't matter what the circumstance is, we always find an imaginative excuse. You name the moment and either I've pulled the excuse or I've heard someone do it:

*"Oh, thank you officer for pointing out that I was doing ninety in a thirty mile an hour zone. It's a new motor cycle, I wasn't sure which dial was the speedometer and which was the temperature gauge."*

Us guys can stretch our imagination and the limits of credibility beyond that of even Hans Christian Anderson. No matter how silly or implausible the excuse, a man will have a go at trying to pull it off. Even if the woman you're telling it to doesn't believe a word of it, she will appreciate the effort and inventiveness that's been applied. Despite women often saying that they value honesty in a man, in reality they don't all want it — that's right they don't want it and it's often an insult to them to pull that honest crap.

You think I'm taking rubbish? Well tell me which of the following lines your girlfriend would prefer to hear:

a) I never slept with her. I had drunk too much to drive and there was only one bed in the flat.

b) I never slept with her because we were wide awake the whole night doing the nasty. She had drunk so much and fortunately there was only one bed in the flat. Oh yeah, the sex was great.

Anyone who picked line 'b' either has a suicidal instinct or has the kind of girlfriend that I really need to meet. Like I said, a good excuse will always be appreciated over any amount of honesty. Being willing to work your imagination hard to make your woman happy shows consideration. "Yeah I'm late, so what's your problem?" will never ever be welcomed as much as, "Sorry I'm late baby, but on the way here…"

One of the best scenes from the classic Jamaican film *The Harder They Come* is when an old man, having had his clothes stolen by a gunman, is sitting naked on the steps of his house late at night thinking about how he's going to explain his late arrival and lack of clothes to his missus as she calls out of the window: "Yes, take yer time, 'cause I want you to come up with a good one."

Back at the Half Moon, I leaned over and kissed Sweetie on the cheek, sure that this was the right time.

With my gaze fixed on the ceiling above, I began slowly and hesitantly to tell her the deal — the story that I had put off telling her.

"I'm sorry. I should have told you when we first met… but I had forgotten all about it. It was only a one night stand. Years ago. On the ferry over to Sweden. She said there was no need for a johnnie, that she was on the pill. I trusted her. Of course she was on the pill. She had to have been on the pill. I mean, if you don't have trust, you can't get out of bed in the mornings, can you? If you lose your faith in love, what's left? Sex. So you keep sleeping around and losing more trust and sleeping around and losing more faith…

| | | | | |
|---|---|---|---|---|
| they went on a trip | then both | but she asked him to go faster | and reached the point of no return | wear protection |
| then to the restaurant | then the other | she refused | But he lost his self-control | for not making a woman pregnant |
| he invited her to have a coffee | she spreaded one leg | he suggested some other positions | she wasn't on the pill | The morale: |
| he took the plunge | and she laid down on the bed | he discovered that she wasn't a virgin | She hadn't told him the truth: | he wanted to die |
| his adrenaline started pumping | she told him she was on the pill | she shouted Stop! | his world crumbled | |
| he felt desire burning inside him | he took her to his house | he went in and out | When she saw all the colours of the rainbow, | he had 2 children! |
| he saw a woman sleeping | they did different activities | he penetrated her | 3.5m | from the hospital |
| One day, he was walking | he reaction was immediate | she made comments on his equipment | | she called him 9 months later |

"But she called me up a few weeks later, talking 'bout how she's pregnant and how she was just calling to let me know that and to tell me that she's going overseas and that I would never see or hear from her or the baby. Before I could say anything, she'd put the phone down. I didn't have her number, her address, nothing. I didn't even have her name.

"Because I've never heard anything, I assumed that it didn't happen. I never thought I would have to send out a search party. But you know what the deal is, these nightmares are so vivid. I guess it's better to learn earlier than later. I've come a long way since it happened, and I would love to get to that 'finish line' and close this chapter once and for all."

It is amazing how I immediately felt better physically, mentally and spiritually for finally being able to tell it like it was.

Sweetie stares blankly. "So you lied to me. When I asked you if you have any kids out there, you told me no. You lied."

"But how was I to know for sure that I'd been robbed?"

"Robbed? I guess you could say that. When a woman's hormones start raging... well, I feel sorry for any man in her path. Because once a woman has got her mind made up there isn't a thing a man can do to dissuade her. I know women who decided to stop taking the pill, just like that. Not a word to their partners. Quite apart from that, D, where does all this leave me and the kids?"

That threw me. I didn't know what to say. You would at least think she would've been like, "That's f***ed up!" But no, she just held it down. So I picked up the thread from the rewind.

*"Pregnant?!* I was still in shock, unable to speak. She said she was having the kid and… then she was gone. Just like that. All she left me was a dial tone. Never did hear from her again. I can't even go to sleep without it haunting me. That's why I'm coming clean. I can't take it anymore. The nightmares… every night… Why has all this come back to haunt me? Am I supposed to be learning something from it?"

Sweetie stares blankly. "So where does that leave me and the kids?"

"But I'm pretty sure it was a wind-up. I'm 99.9999 per cent sure I don't have another kid out there."

"So… you're telling me you've got another kid out there," Sweetie confirmed.

"No. Probably not. I don't think so. On the real, doh, back in the day I played it safe for the most part and usually had a condom on. But just suppose I do have a

kid out there somewhere? Jeez, he'd be nineteen now.
What if I get a knock on the door some day? Even though
he is a kid I never wanted, even though he is a complete
stranger, I couldn't slam the door in his face could I?
What would I do? What would you do? I have little
enough time for Chardonnay and Cartier as it is. Am I
suddenly supposed to make room for this new person?
This stranger. I wonder who he looks like? I wonder who
he takes after? What if I don't like him? What if I
positively dislike him, how could I undo the work of
nineteen years? Then there are all the practical things. I'd
have to introduce him to the members of my family.
They'd want to know why they were meeting him for the
first time. I would have to explain everything — the
sordid details. How would that make them feel? How
heart-warming to grow up to discover that your mother
tricked your father. And what about the future? What if
this kid wants his children to meet the grandfather who
doesn't know their father? What if he's already got kids
the same age as our kids? What will I say when
Chardonnay and Cartier demand to know how come
they're aunts so early in life to kids their own age? It's
one big problem. Ever since that phone was hung up on
me, I've been left wondering. It's hung over me all these
years and never quite left me. Even simple things like

filling in the 'how many children do you have' box on the census forms... Well, you don't know do you?"

"No," Sweetie agreed, "you don't. So D, where does all this leave me and the kids? Supposing something happens to us whilst we're over here, some child we don't even know could inherit everything."

# RENT-A-DREAD

*Maureen, 38, conceived her daughter, Marie, during a brief affair. She decided not to use contraception, in the hope that she would become pregnant. 'I didn't consider it a deceitful act,' she says. 'He never asked me if I was on the pill. Like many men, I suspect he presumed.' She has had no contact with Marie's father since. 'He has no redress as far as I'm concerned. He didn't wear a condom or take measures to stop the spill.'*

It's just a fact of life that, unless he is a monk, every man has, to a greater or lesser degree, wondered whether there could be a child he doesn't know about. Some men may have very good reason to be wondering. For others it's more of a vague, almost philosophical, notion than a biological reality.

To be honest, I hadn't even considered the legal implications of another child. From our suite at the Half

Moon, I made a long distance call to London — my spar
Steve, who is also my lawyer. I gave him the scenario as
delicately as I could:

"…And I haven't got a number or an address. All I've
got is a naked pic of her."

*"So you've got an illegitimate child out there. Where does
that leave Sweetie and the kids? Suppose this child turns up at
your door, how would you deal with it?"*

"What can I do, man? I can slam the door shut, but I
can't run away from it. It's a life sentence, that's what
I've got."

*"You and all the other millions of men who scattered their
seed far and wide and recklessly in their youth. Now the
chickens are coming home to roost. You've only got yourself to
blame. If you had abstained, like I did until I got married, you
would know that all your kids were accounted for."*

"Steve, man, you're supposed to be my spar, my
bredrin. Why are you giving me grief? Just because
you're Mister 'Cum Correct', you don't have to have a
pop at me. I need advice not chastisement."

*"In that case, you need to sort out your will quick time.
Because whether the kid's out there or not, you have to live
with the possibility for the rest of your life. He could make a
claim on your estate after your death."*

"But that's ridiculous. How can a total stranger have

any claim over me? My current will already says I want everything to go to 'my children'. By that I mean Chardonnay and Cartier. I'm not a rich man. If my estate has to be divided three ways instead of two, there won't be much left for any of them."

*"You need to sort out your will,"* Steve repeated. *"If you leave your estate to 'my children' then anyone who could show they were your child would have a claim. You never know, that might mean sharing out your meagre estate between 97 kids."*

"But what do I owe to a kid I never knew I had?"

*"You owe him everything."*

"But I was conned…"

*"I know exactly where you're coming from. I told my wife 'no more kids' then she forgot to take the pill one morning and 'boom-boom-boom' I'm going to be a daddy again. Conned or not, the law does not excuse you from the responsibility of taking precautions yourself."*

So even the law thinks I was in the wrong! But surely I'm not the villain here, I'm the victim. If that woman did intentionally use my sperm to have a child, then I was robbed. Doesn't a man have rights over his sperm and how it's used? Do men have to assume that any woman they sleep with is a potential sperm bandit? If that's the case we can never trust any woman anymore.

Anger can be dangerous. If you harbour it, it will slowly

eat away at you and blind you to what's really going on.

"Sweetie, I swear, the girl didn't mean anything to me. She told me she'd not had sex for a month and I felt sorry for her. I was just trying to help out..."

It was the last night of our stay in Jamaica and Sweetie had been acting funny all night, refusing to give me a squeeze. She didn't want to hear my excuses.

"Was it my fault? Did I do something wrong?"

She looked at me like 'How can you be so stupid? What meaningless, self-inflicted psychological trauma are you going through now?'

I gotta tell the truth. My love for Sweetie got tested that night. While I can understand someone getting vexed if they stumbled on their partner playing 'hide the salami', I can't see how a brief encounter so many years ago should land me in the dog house. I mean, long gone are the days when a child out of wedlock was a family scandal. A family scandal nowadays is if you *don't* have a child out of wedlock.

Sometimes I wonder if we take all this infidelity business far too seriously. I used to be the jealous sort until I went out with a girl who I discovered was so slack that she should have had a parking meter fixed to her knickers. She had so many male 'friends' that if I was going to kill her lover, half the male population in west

London would need to be eradicated.

Sweetie wasn't listening to any of it. She was in a mood, contrary, and I was going to have to pay.

"What's wrong, honey?" I asked.

"I'm hungry. No I'm not, I'm sleepy, I'm going to bed," she said suddenly as I made moves to get some more of that sweetness she'd been giving me all week. "On second thoughts, I am so not ready to go to bed. I either want to go to a club, or maybe even a restaurant so that we can talk."

"No. I don't feel like talking. I want to make love."

"Not tonight, D. I have too much on my mind. I have a lot of things worrying me, you know."

"Me too," I said, "but then if we make love it will take a lot of the things off your mind."

"Maybe yours, but not mine. You think all you have to do is jump on me and that solves everything. Well, that doesn't solve anything."

I felt a lump form in my throat. I didn't know what she was planning, but I knew she had something in mind. Some payback.

She went and got her hair done that afternoon — got some twists put into the crop (it took several hours but will only last for four days before it starts getting frizzy again). Then she spent the next couple of hours trying on her entire honeymoon wardrobe before deciding on what to wear. She knows how that winds me up. And to rub it in, she would ask for my opinion with every change of costume.

My opinion was *Yeah, that looks good on you. Pick any rhatid dress and let's get out of here! This is the last night of our honeymoon, I'd rather not spend it at a fashion show.*

But what I actually said was, "Yes, that flimsy sarong looks great on you."

We eventually climbed into the rental car that had been sitting in the hotel car park for nearly a week without being driven, and drove into downtown Mo'Bay.

How come when you're out on the razzle you never see any fine women, but when you're out with your woman you see babes so fine that you would just like to look without getting slapped? Honestly. Sweetie caught me salivating more than once. She didn't seem to care, but I was just not confident enough to risk it for a biscuit.

We went to an open air cinema first. That was an experience in itself. While the film was in progress, the rest of the audience treated us to a highly audible live commentary of the action on the screen.

Comments such as:

"Lawd, me frighten."

"What a way 'ooman wicked, eeh man."

"Yuh see 'im, 'im fe dead."

"Nah man, 'flim' star cyaan dead before the end."

Before heading back to the Half Moon, we stopped at the famous Sweet Spices Club to fill our bellies with some home cooking — fried chicken and oxtail — and to vibes up with a little reggae in our jeggay. Cars lined both sides of the road as we approached. A hand-painted sign above the entrance announced: *No prostitutes, touts, hoodlums, teef etc. etc.*

Of course, no night on the town in Mo'Bay is complete without the local gigolos — the world-renowned rent-a-dreads, a very nasty creature with a set of gold teeth, whatever senses he had knocked out of him, and the inclination to "wuk a granny, if the dolla*h*s ah run right." May I suggest that anyone looking for such an individual should have their foreign currency at the ready to draw the rent-a-dread's attention. Green cards, credit cards, Moschino and other brand-name jeans will also do nicely.

Sweet Spices was packed inside. Music, subdued lighting and a flickering strobe greeted us. A couple of strippers were on stage dancing (surrounded by some slim shady type guys trying to get a closer look). The ugly stripper had a thick batty and big old breasts. The other was on the slender side or, to be honest, downright skinny with a compact batty and a cute face. But I didn't really notice, because I'm a married man now. Besides, I was with my missus.

After a minute or two of searching, I finally found an empty table.

We hadn't been there long when a dread in a Reggae Boyz football top started whispering something into Sweetie's ear, his eyes hidden behind dark glasses. I was at the bar sorting out the refreshments. When you're as tense as I was, you're able to read someone's lips at thirty feet.

"Hello," he said, a sly smile on his chops, "you doing anyt'ing special after you leave here tonight?"

"Nothing special, why?" Sweetie asked. "Have you got something in mind?"

"Maybe," the dread said, sweet enough for her to take the bait. "I can show you a few sights, y'know. You have a car? Let's go for a drive. We could go for a midnight picnic or somet'ing, or just chill."

"That sounds like a good idea."

Grinning from ear to ear, the dread turned to Sweetie. "Shall we leave now, or are you wit' someone?"

He looked over at me ponderously. So did Sweetie. I held up my hand in a sort of 'Hail Caesar, well met' half-wave.

"Can my husband come too?" she said after a long

pause.

"Well… a highly unusual t'ing dat. But I guess so," he said uncertainly. "It's highly unusual. Okay, stay here. Me soon come."

"Who was that man?" I asked Sweetie, when I returned with the drinks.

"You mean the man in the dark glasses?"

"Yes… that one."

"Oh… him."

"You looked at him good?"

"No. I just glimpsed him."

It was something in the way she lied, made me wish I hadn't told her about that time on the ferry. If only we could go back to the way things were before. I had a feeling that it was too late for that.

We are all familiar with women claiming 'my man ain't no good', but I think the words 'no good' are often mistaken to mean rogue, womaniser etc. Sadly, all men are created equal. If you want a committed man, look in a mental hospital. But what about if you want a committed woman? Women have a lot to answer for. Half of all divorced people are women! A shocking statistic if I ever saw one. Of course, it's us guys who are left to pick up the pieces. *(NB: the best place to pick up pieces is at clubs and wine bars).* That's why nobody will ever win the battle of the sexes — there's too much fraternizing with the enemy.

Back at Sweet Spices, I still didn't know which way to turn.

"Sweetie, how about a dance?"

She agreed. Somewhat reluctantly. I held her hand and moved towards the dance floor. Right on cue the deejay dropped a UK lovers selection, like it was dedicated to us. Carroll Thompson, the queen of lovers, oozed through the speakers:

*I'm so sorry, I didn't mean to make you blue*
*I'm so sorry, I didn't mean to make you cry*
*Oh no, oh no-o-o-o-o...*

*I really loved you*
*With a love anyone would be proud of*
*But I knew it would happen someday*
*I really tried my best to stay*
*It was just, you didn't understand me*
*So you weren't sure how to love me*
*It's not your fault, it's all mine*
*I guess I was a little mixed up inside*

*I'm so sorry, I didn't mean to make you blue*
*I'm so sorry, I didn't mean to make you cry*

*Oh no, oh no-o-o-o-o...*

I pulled Sweetie close, confident that the lyrics would soothe her ire. With one aesthetic eye on the rest of the talent in the club, I echoed Carroll's words in her ear.

The custom's guy was right — the weed is better, the weather is warmer, the clubs stay open later, and the women in Jamaica are friendly. Very friendly. Not stuck up the arse. In a manner of speaking, that is, because in some ways they are stuck right up the arse when you consider how short their shorts are. Personally, I don't see anything wrong with it. I think the batty rider is the best thing that ever happened to the country. The island is so hot that a batty rider is a blessing. I mean, you've got to admire a woman who's prepared to risk cutting herself in two with a piece of string separating the cheeks of her behind. In JA it's not a question of 'Does this make my batty look big?' It's more 'I hope so.' If all the women in Jamaica wore batty riders, I don't think I'd ever leave.

I know, I know, I'm married now. I must be strong and not submit to the wicked will of my a-dick-shun. It's just that every now and then you see a woman who makes your pants bulge. I've been married a week and, I swear, I haven't slept with anyone but my wife. Not that I haven't felt the urge, urging me to, "Come with me, son, and join the dark side. Come, feel the power…"

Please, slap me on the mouth if I get lustful thoughts again.

It seems that Sweetie had set aside this special time to humiliate me in public. She slapped me hard on the mouth. "Sometimes I just want to wrap my fingers around your neck and…" she yelled in frustration.

Most of the dancers on the floor gave us a wide birth. A few of them moved closer to see the fun. The deejay's laughter echoed into the mic.

I didn't have to ask what the slap was for. I knew. I didn't take it to heart. Nevertheless I had to say something to let her know I was still breathing. I mean, here we are supposed to be having fun and kicking back and we're just about to get thrown in jail for fighting. So I'm like, 'Peace treaty, before you seriously hurt somebody'. "Look," I said, "you're drunk. Why don't we go back to the hotel?"

I shouldn't have said that. She turned my other cheek and slapped that too.

*Ouch!* That was cold, considering the circumstances.

"Look, I'm sorry. I know you feel like I duped you. I should have told you that I might have another kid out…"

Sweetie wasn't interested in what I had to tell her or

any other excuses. She just wasn't feeling me. She simply stared and went about her business.

"Baby, you really don't know what you're upset about," I tried to reason. "Anger is irrational sometimes. You really need a punching bag... you just need to kick in a few walls or run some laps or something. When a woman's got something on her mind — hell — she gotta 'exhale'."

I know... It was intended as a joke. Don't get me wrong, I can be sweet, caring, loving etc, and I believe in good old fashioned loving, but you got to have a laugh when you're in the dog house, innit?

The said dread inched his way through the crowd and stepped up, indicating for Sweetie to follow him. Can you believe, she actually followed him. I followed too. I mean, what else could I do?

In the car park outside the venue, the dread, who introduced himself as 'Bongo' leaned against our rental and, ignoring me, told Sweetie his plan.

"I can show you something nice... *real* nice," he assured her.

She nodded too willingly. "There is this one thing I've been wanting to check out since I've been in JA."

"Come nuh," he said, opening the rear passenger door.

I couldn't believe what was going on. I was ready to

hurt somebody, but Bongo looked like he could hurt me bad. "Haven't I seen you somewhere before?" I asked, trying to remember the evil faces I had seen on 'Jamaica's Most Wanted' on the hotel TV.

The dread turned to me. Took off his dark glasses for the first time. Talk about 'red eye'. The guy's pupils were blazing. The only thing missing were the horns on his head.

"Take a look at yourself," he sneered. " 'Bout me favour s'maddy. No, suh, me nuh favour nobody."

I couldn't let my wife go off without me, could I? So we piled into the rental car and headed out onto the road, me at the wheel. Sweetie beside me, Bongo in the back rolling a bighead spliff.

"Yaow, 'bout the weed — never leave home without your own supply. Especially if you know is soca you headin' for... me nah jester. The herb is spiritual, religious. Legalise it — YES — so we can all have some. Especially those of us who do not imbibe alcohol. Me nah go ah jail fe ganja no more and it would be nice not to have to hide the holy indica at my age, it's undignified. Anyhow, Black Star Liner soon come. 'Cause when music lick, you feel no pain! This is why dem must legalize the weed an' set up a commission to increase potency an usage for I and I."

I didn't have a clue what he was talking about. I wasn't listening. "Just stick to the driving," I kept telling myself.

I find that when someone's high and you're not, you can't reach him on his level. You've got to climb up there and meet him high in the smoke. Sweetie (who never usually smoked) was already up there, so I had no choice but to join them, because Bongo was never without a spliff or rolling a next one.

"Ah, Mr Bongo, can I get some of that herb? It smells like it's the dog's bollocks," I said. I needed time to figure things out. Little did I know that it really was the dog's bollocks.

As we tripped through the bright Jamaican moonlight, Bongo pointed out the local hot spots, purring his words from right behind Sweetie's neck. I could feel my heart beating. Then, as Sweetie turned around for confirmation on something, their lips brushed, I'm sure of it. I wanted to say something, but I couldn't speak. I felt my body stiffen as the herb kicked in and the whole world slowed in motion. "So, Bongo, tell me, what time do you have to go home to your woman and eleven pickney?" was all I said when finally I managed to squeeze out some words.

By now we were all blazed out of our minds.

I should have known that he would have rehearsed a

whole routine.

"*My* woman?" he repeated with a touch of astonishment. "Inna this great generation of independent women, the chances of finding a woman who is content with being my personal woman are slim t'raas. As for the pickney dem, I'm not stupid enough to spread my seed until I find that woman. Seen?"

Sweetie was duly impressed. "Wish more men were as sensible as you," she said, cutting her eye at me. "You ever been to foreign, Bongo?"

"Yeah, man, how ya mean," came the reply. "Me born ah Inglann, y'know, in Aberdeen. See me yahso, me *h*english, but me live ah Jamaica."

We pulled over outside a roadside bar where an argument ensued between Bongo and the vendor about his 'for foreigners only' priced beers and cigarettes. But the man wasn't budging. Sweetie and I were tourists, therefore we would have to pay the tourist rate. Bongo shrugged his shoulders, after all he wasn't paying. He turned to me. "You 'ave money?"

We ordered a couple of Heinekens whilst Sweetie availed herself of the bathroom facilities. As we waited for her, the dread and I sat down outside the shack to get crunked up while listening to the sounds of crickets in the night air.

"You want me to find a gal fe you?" Bongo asked, passing me a spliff tail.

"No," I said, pulling out my wallet, "I want you to disappear into the night. I want you to take these J$5,000 to help you pay the rent and feed those pickney you told Sweetie you never had, and I want you to leave me and my wife alone."

"Blood an' fiyah!" he exclaimed, "what a bumboclaat. Jealous you ah jealous. Me nuh want your money, but me ah tek it anyway, 'cause me nah kill no man fe no woman. Seen? Me nah fight people over somet'ing stupid. It nuh mek no sense, but me nah fight it. Mek it ten t'ousand," he said, holding up his hands in front of my face to emphasise the amount with the stubby rectangular fingers of both hands.

I fished in my wallet for another J$5,000 and handed it over.

No sooner had he taken my money than Sweetie returned and insisted that he stay put and not leave. I had to play it off like it didn't bother me. So six Heinekens, a couple of spliffs and one bun and cheese later, we rolled out on the road again, with me ten g's poorer.

The herb was serious, crept up on you nice and slow. Sweetie was now in the back seat with Bongo, feeling 'irie'. "I want somebody to make love to me so good that our bodies literally melt into each other," she purred.

I was sure that I heard Bongo turn to her with a sly smile and say, "It's all set. Truss me." But I was too stoned to be sure.

The headlights pierced the tropical night as we plunged into the darkness of the coast road. The rental car hurtled forward as I stepped on the accelerator.

"Take it easy," Sweetie said, "we're not in any hurry."

"Keep your eyes on the road," Bongo added. Did his left hand just gently squeeze Sweetie's right breast, or is it the chronic imagining it? A sudden feeling of loneliness overcame me.

I slowed down to fifty, negotiating the road along the seafront. Bongo was whispering into Sweetie's ear as he rolled a conehead spliff. She was giggling uncontrollably.

"I know a lovely beach, yah know," Bongo barked at me. "Drive out 'til you see a sign sayin' Coc'nut Grove."

After a drive that seemed to take an eternity (the usual route was closed due to an accident) along winding country lanes, Bongo showed me the turning and we travelled down a narrow dirt track, past some little huts lit only with kerosene lamps. Then I turned one last corner and there it was before us. Unspoiled. The most beautiful deserted beach, lined with coconut

trees, mango and breadfruit trees. Two canoes pulled up
onto the beach were the only indication that anyone had
ever been there. The white sand shimmered and
twinkled in the full moonlight, which cast a long golden
line across the dark water.

"Isn't that a beautiful and romantic sight?" Sweetie
gushed.

"Oh yes... it's beautiful," I agreed.

Bongo grinned. I switched off the ignition. Sweetie
climbed out, ran down to the water and tested it with
her toes.

"Come on in... it's lovely," she called out as she
tossed aside her flimsy sarong immodestly.

I caught Bongo admiring her nakedness with a smile.
He didn't hesitate to join her. He kicked off his sandals
and cast off his T-shirt and, in just his shorts, bodysurfed
over to her, somehow, still rolling a next spliff.

"Ooh!" I heard Sweetie shriek several times as they
tumbled together between the waves, then she laughed
loud and long, her elation carried out to sea by the
breeze but not speedily enough.

I heard her pleasure all right. Sounded like: *You can
ring my be-e-ell, ring my bell!* I couldn't let Bongo get
away with it. This was my wife after all. But what could
I do? I didn't want to say that I was scared of being in the
sea at night. I love swimming, but only in daylight. I felt

a twinge of fear as I moved closer to the water's edge. Then I felt panic, terror.

"Sweetie," I called, "don't go far out. We don't know this beach, and there might be anything in the water... sharks."

At first I thought she never heard me, then I realised that she was laughing at me. They both were.

"Come out of the water, Sweetie. I don't like that shark business," I repeated.

"There are no sharks in here, silly," she replied, all giggly.

"Well, there might be... so come on," I insisted. "Sweetie, we have to leave. NOW."

"*You* leave..." Bongo called back.

*What the f...?* I couldn't believe what I just heard. After all the money I'd given him. Who did he think...?

"Sweetie, let's go," I called out again. "It's been a long day."

"Where are we going?" she called back. "Not to the hotel. It's only three in the morning, too early yet. I don't know about you, but I want to swim. Come on, don't be a spoilsport, you're on your honeymoon. It's a sultry moonlit night, we're on a beautiful romantic beach, it's a magic moment, what could be better than a refreshing dip in the sea?"

I couldn't leave my wife there with Bongo. I've heard all the rent-a-dread stories, knew that Jamaica was the land of wood (or 'hood' if you prefer) and water, and was pretty certain that Bongo would try and give her the wickedest slam if I gave him half the chance. With Sweetie off her head on such good weed, there's no telling what might happen. It's all about trust. I should have been able to trust my woman, but recent events had made me doubt whether I could ever trust any woman more than 99.99999999999 percent. Which means I probably can't trust 'em at all.

I'm on the edge, in need of mental relief. Sweetie was still refusing to come out of the water, and I was still too frightened to go in and get her. I didn't want to piss her off any more than I had already. I had never seen her in this mood before, so I decided to go back to the car and sit it out... and smoke the rest of Bongo's stash while I waited.

It was definitely the good stuff. The best stuff. The stuff that catapults you into outta space.

We're told that men are from Mars and women hail from Venus. I can't say that I'm an expert on astronomy, although I do think that Russell Grant is better than Patrick Moore. But I know that Mars and Venus are further apart than, say, Hackney and White City. What I don't know is whether there's any life on Venus.

As I stand here in me space suit surveying the landscape of Venus, t'ings look kinda bleak and desolate. Where there was once life now everything looks dead.

Now don't get me wrong, I'm not trying to excuse poor workmanship or anything of the kind, but there are some customers who are very hard to please if you get my drift. I've come to the conclusion that a lot of women are confused about what they really want from a man. They spout on about wanting a sensitive man who will make love to them and hold and cherish them, but play that kind of role and I'll bet my butt dollar that they'll think of you as being as interesting in the sack as weathermen are on the telly.

*Exaggerating?* Listen, I've been there, done it, and have still got the commemorative mug on the mantelpiece, my friend. I've been married to Sweetie a week and been playing Mr Nice Guy for years, now look where that got me. Forget all that soft and sensitive bit. That's what women say they want, but don't believe a word of it. Be Mr Nice Guy and I'll bet that you end up watching your woman frollocking in the ocean with some rent-a-dread. Harsh as it might be to say, too many women don't appreciate the sensitivity they claim they want.

I'm a bit of a softie, so I don't take easily to the bad

bwoy bedroom bully role. But blow me, (pun purely coincidental) if it hasn't been one of the most necessary roles I've had to master. Shakespeare said 'the world's a stage and we are mere actors' or some such t'ing. If that's the case, my advise to any soft and sensitive geezers out there is to start method acting the role of 'dungeon master'. That and a good knowledge of handcuffs will do more for your bedroom appreciation than anything else.

So there I am, sitting in the car, under some good chron, daydreaming about being back at work doing no work. Yes, I'm in a chillin' mood, mellowing out, when I start thinking about how things could have been so different if I had missed that ferry to Sweden.

By rights I shouldn't have been on that sailing. After all I had already missed the train to the ferry, which is why I had to scout Tottenham in a hurry for a ride. Of all the bad luck, the ferry had engine trouble and was still in port when I finally got to Felixstowe an hour late. I thought it was my lucky day, of course, like my life depended on making it to that boat. How things could have been so different if I had observed the Nazarene code and kept my zip up, subjugated my penis, and turned my back on that moment of forbidden pleasure.

I know a man is not supposed to cry, but sitting in that car on that beautiful beach, I started crying for no

apparent reason. Scared the poo outta me. Scared me awake. I woke up in a cold sweat, thinking about Bongo. I knew I recognized him. He was the spitting image of *her* — the same sloping eyes (a legacy of her Chinese-Jamaican heritage), the same angular forehead (a legacy of her African heritage) and that bowlegged gait. *But I thought she couldn't have any kids?* Those genes couldn't have come from any other woman but Lady P. Bongo was the right age, too, to be her son. Aberdeen was the giveaway. How many other black men could have been born in Aberdeen about nineteen years ago? But the really frightening thing were his hands. Only one set of genes could have produced those rectangular digits. I looked down at my hands...

*Aaaaaaaaaaaaaaaaggggggggggghhhhhhhh!*

I jumped out of the car, raced down to the water's edge screaming, "Sweetie! Swee-teeeee!!"

But Bongo and Sweetie were nowhere to be seen. The water was too shallow for them to have been washed out to sea. She can't say I didn't warn her about the sharks.

"Swee-teeeee!!" I called again. No answer. I searched for them a little while longer before giving up the ghost and deciding to leave in the rental car.

Back at the Half Moon, I tried to keep myself awake by reading a recent copy of *Cosmopolitan* that Sweetie had brought with her on the honeymoon. Why do male celebrities always feel the need to strip off their clothes for these bleeding photo shoots in women's magazines? It's not big and it's not clever. Mind you, seeing the size of the bunch of grapes needed to hide TV chef Ainsley Harriott's dong in one pic, I might have to rephrase that expression just a little. I wonder if his schlong really is that long, or is he just bragging?

If his middle wicket actually is the size of a four and a half pound bunch of grapes then you can guess who advised Linford Christie on packing *his* 'lunchbox'. I have to give Ainsley full credit for being such a successful cook. How he doesn't get it trapped in oven doors or falling into mixing bowls is beyond me.

Yet even Ainsley's donkey dickie couldn't stop me thinking about Sweetie with Bongo Dred. Why oh why did I leave them together in the sea? Why did I smoke some more herb and fall asleep when I should have been keeping an eye on Bongo? I just hope Sweetie doesn't do anything we'll all regret before I get a chance to tell her that I might have TWO kids out there that I didn't know about.

# TWELVE INCHES OF PLEASURE

*There was this couple that were married for twenty years, and every time they had sex the husband always insisted on turning off the lights and doing it in absolute darkness. Well, after twenty years the wife felt this was stupid. She figured she would break him out of the crazy habit. So one night, while they were in the middle of having sex, she turns on the lights. She looks down and sees her husband holding a cucumber. She gets very upset. "You bast\*\*\*d," she screams at him. "Is this how you've been deceiving me all these years? You better explain yourself!"*

*The husband looks her straight in the eyes and says calmly, "Sure, I'll explain the cucumber if you can explain our three kids."*

Ladies, can you imagine being in bed with your best friend's boyfriend when you hear her coming through the front door? What would you do? Well, for Ms X the decision the boyfriend made on her behalf was to have long lasting repercussions. Rather than get caught, he told her to jump out of the window. In blind panic she did. The only problem was that they were four floors up in an east London tower block. The poor girl was paralysed in the fall and is now confined to a wheelchair for the rest of her life.

That I swear is a true story. Some of you reading this will probably know who I'm talking about. Meanwhile, on the other side of London, a geezer returns home early from work to find his wife having it off with his nephew. He goes ballistic and stabs and kills both the wife and her lover. As a finishing touch he cuts off his relative's gonads. Again, true story, and the funny thing of it all is that, after a period of time in an institution, he ends up marrying the sister of his wife.

There are lots of other stories about the perils of infidelity, because if there's one thing that gets people raging it's catching out a partner when s/he strays. I mean, can you imagine how afraid that guy must have been of how his girlfriend was going to react that he tells someone to jump from four storeys up?

Black folk don't ramp when it comes to finding a partner on the job. But English guys are different. One English girl once told me how her boyfriend caught her

banging the next door neighbour. "What did you do?" I
asked aghast. She told him to close the bedroom door
and wait outside the flat 'til she had got dressed. He of
course, like a stiff-upper wimp, did as he was told. Now,
can you imagine a brotha behaving in such a way? "Oh
sorry, Yvonne, how rude of me to interrupt you while
you are having intercourse with our neighbour. Yes,
m'dear, I don't mind waiting outside while you finish
off. Our neighbour seems to be doing a most excellent
job. Is there anything I can get you from the newsagents
while I'm down there? I think I'll buy a copy of the
highway code to read on the front step while you're
finishing off."

Yeah, you can but dream, ladies, because you and I
know that it's not going to happen in tha 'hood. The gun
fight at the OK Coral would look like a tea party
compared to what would really happen if your black
significant other caught you playing away.

I am a semi-light sleeper and if I woke up in the
middle of something like that I would not be a happy
camper. Of course, if I was to go crazy with the machete
I would probably end up being treated as if I had killed
a complete stranger in the street. In Britain the law
doesn't make any special favours to those who catch
others with their pants/panties around someone else's
ankles. 'Crime of passion' don't cut it with a culture

which believes that to even show your displeasure at the situation would be bad form.

In France, however, they don't play cricket. Traditionally, they've had a very different view. The French practically invented infidelity but they are also very understanding of those who kill their partner's lover. It is not unknown for these killers to walk free from French courts, or at the worst to serve two year sentences.

But is there any purpose served in actually killing your other half's lover? No, far better to dash your partner, walk away then go and sleep with his/her best mate. What's good for the goose and all that...

Now, Lady P was originally from Jamaica, via Brixton. She wasn't exactly *my* woman. At least not exclusively. She had a husband too, as a back-up, just in case I was unavailable.

She had ended up in Aberdeen after marrying a Scottish Lord and moving up to his castle not far from the city. She now spoke in a weird mix of an accent that contained some 'dirty souf' (London) brogue, a smattering of Scottish twang and a really terrible upper class drawl afflicted with terrible delusions of grandeur. In short, she had developed a real snootchie-bootchie attitude towards her roots. I was hitchhiking on a quiet highland road when she pulled up in her Merc and offered me a lift.

She must have been 40/45. Despite her 'class' she had a gold-crown smile. I had barely sat down in the nicely perfumed interior before she kicked the accelerator and stuck the boot in with a 'black men ain't no good' routine. As far as she was concerned, men my colour were low-down, lazy backside, no job having, no class having, no credit having drug dealers with only three goals in life — to own the latest trainers, maintain their hair and drive the latest car — while spending their lives sleeping around with every other female. In fact, she blamed brothas for everything that ever went wrong in her life.

"Too many bad experiences. That's why I married a white man, the whitest man on earth. Black men are irresponsible, they can't take care of their children, their four baby mama's, their job, their life, and definitely not themselves. So how could they possibly take care of me?"

I was ready to jump out the car, but she insisted that I stay. "You're different. I like you. You remind me of when I was young and stupid."

As she drove, she insisted that all she was trying to do was help the black man in general and me in particular, become a better person, while insinuating that even if the black man was to succeed, he could never be equal to the trophy of a white man that had made her the lady of the manor and its thousands of adjoining acres.

"I am just not attracted to black men," she continued. "They just don't do it for me anymore. After all it is my preference, and I am entitled to that."

It turns out, she had had only two black boyfriends in her life. Both turned out to be playas. Since then she had dated about six white guys, including her husband, who had also messed around and seen other women. Now what conclusion does Lady P come to? All men are rats who can't be trusted? No. She decides that all black guys are wotless, and carries on only seeing white guys.

Why is it that so many black women seem so hell bent on waging this 'black man bad' war? Some spend their time whingeing on about how this man or that man disrespected them. Their relationships with their brothaman have made them bitter and angry people and we must all suffer as a result. I've heard lots of white women talk about bad experiences they've had from white guys. But do you hear them saying that white men are all bad? Of course you don't. They might have a pop at men in general, but they don't attempt to write off a group of millions because of their experiences with a handful.

Last time I went to the optician he was all sold out of rose-tinted specs so don't accuse me of surveying the landscape with some sort of distorted vision. I know all about the wasters, the crackheads, the woman beaters and the absentee serial baby fathers. But why should the majority be tried for the sins of the minority? Why has every black guy got to be labelled as a 'waste of time'?

I heard a friend of an ex-girlfriend saying in front of her eight year old son. "Black men need help. They are a disgrace." She was commenting on the recent shootings in London and seemed quite happy to blame every black man for the nasty deeds of a group of scumbags who are probably less than a couple of hundred in number. She of course is black. So what is her son to make of the world when the main teacher in his life comes out with a statement like that? How is something like that going to help his future self-esteem? My questions are of course rhetorical. I don't need to know what the answers are because I know them already.

We all know there is good and bad in every race and every group in this world. We hear about all the bad things that are supposed to be the way of the black man. Wouldn't it be nice, just for once, if a little armistice could be put into operation. Stop the labelling, the sweeping generalisations, the stereotypes, the recriminations and the blaming. Deal with each person as an individual and give peace a chance. Like most others, I'm not a saint but I sure as hell ain't the devil.

Life is full of tragic irony. After her outburst, who could predict that I would end up sleeping with Miss P that night? You see, all was not hunky dory back at the manor. Let's put it this way: his lordship and her ladyship were not enjoying conjugal relations. Not since she failed to deliver a son and heir, or even a daughter. According to her, he was having it off with one of his tenant farmer's daughters. Lady P had tried everything else to save her marriage and now, in a desperate attempt to tame him, had brought me in as the whip to beat her husband with. But I didn't know any of this when she invited me to save the price of a bunk bed in the local youth hostel by staying the night in my own suite at their home. As every student knows, there is such a thing as a free lunch. So I accepted the offer. I knew she was barmy, though. So I kept my rucksack close by for a quick getaway, just in case she decided to nip round the back of the castle and take a standing piss up against the wall.

*Fool. She's nuts and you're staying the night? Chimp.*

The castle must have been worth millions. A real fairy tale Norman one with a moat around it and a drawbridge. Inside was very modern though. It had loads of bedrooms and bathrooms, an indoor pool, built-in jacuzzi and sauna, a gym, games room, smoking room and so on and so on. The great hall downstairs was even big enough to accommodate Lord P's entire clan of six brothers, six sisters twenty-five nieces and nephews, and various uncles and aunts and cousins and their children whenever they all met up for family reunions.

By the time we got there, it was dark. The butler showed me to my suite. Inside, I opened the bedroom window and looked out into the darkness. I saw a shooting star — beautiful — and made a wish. But when I opened my eyes pussy wasn't falling out of the sky.

I went and took a shower.

When I came out of the en suite half an hour later, I was ready to turn in. On my thirty-ninth wink, there was a hesitant knock on the door. A moment later her ladyship slipped in with a couple of G&Ts. I couldn't help but notice her chest threatening to burst out of a rather fetching silk dressing gown.

*Hhmm, should I or shouldn't I? Decisions, decisions.*

"I hope you don't mind," she said, perching on the end of the bed. "I could use the company. Besides, we just might become lifelong friends. I'm really easy to get along with once you learn to worship me."

*That's cool. I'm prepared for the challenge. Lick your lips at me like that one more time and see what happens.*

"What I need is to be respected. That can't be so hard, can it?"

I continued watching, waiting for the right minute, the right move, the right second. Lady P continued confessing the blues.

"You see, it's so hard trusting people. Just when you think someone is all right, they show their real colours and stab you in the back. I seem to set myself up to be stabbed in the back all the damn time. Oh well, you live and learn. I guess I'll learn one of these days."

Lady P. obviously wanted to pour her heart out. So I sat up and put a comforting arm around her in my best bedside manner, trying but not succeeding in taking my eyes and my mind off her breasts.

I played it cool, wondering if I should tell her that I couldn't wait to feel myself inside her, that the possibility of making love to her was consuming my thoughts and that I could feel myself about to pop, crackle and snap with desire. I needed some so bad.

With tears in her eyes, she knocked back both G&Ts in two quick gulps and proceeded to tell me the story of her 'fairy tale' marriage. The drink must have loosened her tongue, because she was surprisingly frank.

It was in bed that her relationship had really lost out. Lord P wanted more than anything in the world to have a child, and so did she. But no matter how they tried, she just didn't seem to be able to become pregnant. He had taken her to three top gynaecologists in New York and they had said that there was nothing they could do for her. She would never get pregnant. Lord P became indignant. Claimed she had duped him into marrying her. He had the hereditary title to think of. Who was he going to pass his inheritance on to? He didn't seem to enjoy making love to her anymore after that. Claimed she no longer turned him on. She had been taking all sorts of pills religiously every day since and enduring all kinds of treatments to prove the doctors wrong, but nothing had happened.

*I wonder how she sounds when she comes? Does she yell or whimper or chat Chinese, or is she silent? I wonder if I can make her scream?*

I've learned that regardless of how hot and steamy a relationship is at first, the passion fades. Eventually. You can get by on charm for about fifteen minutes. After that, you'd better have a huge member or large breasts (but usually not both), or a lot of money like his lordship. At least I had one out of three.

As she crossed and uncrossed her legs nervously, I couldn't help but notice that her muff looked well tuff. She wasn't wearing panties. I felt a stiffness inside my boxers. I pulled her closer, to comfort her. Our lips touched. I pulled away half-heartedly. She pulled my head back and looked deep into my eyes, then thrust her tongue into my mouth and played around in there for a minute before withdrawing hurriedly, as if remembering that she was a married woman and that her husband could burst in at any moment.

"I know you're trying to get in my knickers, but I'm not wearing any. Would you like her ladyship to play with it?" she asked, casting her gaze to my crotch.

I smiled. "Sure. Why not."

I *know*... I should've been thinking with my head and not my crowning glory. *Hmnh?*

"Then beg for it."

"I beg you..."

Before I could say another word, she had gripped my manhood in the glove-like feel of her femininity, jerking in a slow rhythm like a piston, before continuing with her story.

"After I got married, we made love every night. But it's been a year now since we made love at all. And if we're talking since I had an orgasm that wasn't self-induced, November will be three years!! I need someone to work me 'til I say 'stop'."

She squeezed tighter. I groaned, "Take it easy, we have all night. We have all the time in the world." I could feel my whole body becoming rigid. There's only so much excitement an eighteen year old can take. I knew that I was going to shoot off if she didn't ease up.

I tried to take my mind off the inevitable by focusing on the 'diss the black man' programme she was on earlier in the car. I reminded her of it.

"I only disrespected you earlier because I have the hots for you. It's a woman thing, you wouldn't understand."

It's difficult showing your anger when some woman's got your tool clamped in a vice-like grip.

I shouted, "Hey... god-*damn*... jeez... I'm... *cumming*..."

I could feel everything inside me coming out. I couldn't hold back. Eyes closed, I wrapped my arms around Lady P's waist. I squeezed her tight. And then it was like the end of the world. My whole body jerked with release. It gushed out like a disconnected water pipe being turned back on. Breathing hard like an athlete who had just completed the four minute mile, I opened my eyes slowly and smiled at her ladyship.

She got up and stood by the bed. "Right," she said, "now you're just about ready to handle a real woman."

Staring down at me, she ripped off her dressing gown and tossed it over a chair. She stood there naked. My eyes nearly popped out of their sockets, I felt weak and dizzy. Her breasts were torpedoes, firm and pinkish brown, much bigger than I imagined. Before I could admire them any further, she walked to the door and turned off the light. On her return she relieved me of my boxers in one swift movement and, for a moment, we faced each other in the semi-darkness, totally naked, both lightly trembling, my manhood back at a right angle to my body. She pulled me towards her and buried my head in her ample bosom.

"What would your husband think if you had an affair and got caught?" I mumbled with my mouth full.

"Shhhhhhhhhhhh!" she said. "Don't talk, suck."

You won't believe what happened next. The woman lifted up her foot and shoved it in my mouth.

*Told you. C.R.A.Z.Y. Now, try this for size.*

"I said suck!" she ordered.

I felt the form of her toes with my tongue. It actually tasted pretty good, though I'd have to brush my teeth like five times to get rid of the garlic taste.

"Where's your husband right now?"

"Next door," she said.

"Next door!?!"

So she broke down the coup, what she wanted me to do. I was the ace in her pack. She wanted me to scream my head off with enjoyment as she slammed the living daylights outta me.

"Look on it as community service," she suggested half-seriously.

They had been married nearly four years. Now the two of them were barely on speaking terms. His lordship was doing his 'thing' and making it known that he was 'single' and ready to mingle. But in the back of her mind she knew that they might still get back together if she could only get him to appreciate what he was missing.

"I can see your point," I conceded. "I guess that's how it sometimes gets between a husband and wife. But I still think it's full of doo-doo. I can't do it properly with your husband next door."

"Well, nothing is going to stop me now. I don't f*** just anyone, you know, I chose you. And, believe me, you are going to f*** me."

"Hey, that's not ladylike," I protested.

"Ladylike? I'm no f***ing lady."

"Well you should be."

"Lie down," she commanded. "Lie on your back."

I did exactly as I was told. She knelt down and proceeded to give me the Monica Lewinsky special, going at it like a woman with no teeth vs. corn on the cob. Can you imagine what it feels like to suddenly look down and see a woman slobbing your knob like there's no tomorrow? Or to look into the mirror and see her munching from a reverse angle? You feel powerful. I mean powerless... I really didn't want to play her game by announcing loud and clear that I was being serviced by the lady of the house, but I couldn't help but scream my head off nevertheless as I got that warm feeling all over like a sip of hot chocolate on a cold winter day. I had to stop her half way just to say "great job".

"OK now... turn around."

*Aaaaahhh, doggystyle!*

I smiled, glad I had got this end of the bargain.

"OK, now *you* turn around," I said.

"Beg for it."

"I beg you..."

I didn't know a woman could be so flexible and accommodating. I felt the sweat running down my back. It felt as if the whole world was moving, as if I was flying through galaxies as yet unexplored. *Damn!* This is good. So good it makes you want to take the day off just to think about it.

She, meanwhile, was banging it, grinding it, crushing it, like crazy. She moved and adjusted her clutch, moaning and groaning frantically, "It's... sooo... loooong!"

It's such an ego boost when you have your woman bouncing up and down wildly and screaming like a porno star: "It's sooo long! It's *sooo* long!"

"No, you got it wrong. Not 'long', wrong. You got it wrong. *Soooo* wrong. Wrong hole!!!!!!"

Oh *damn!*

"Now kiss my bum better," she ordered, loud enough for the whole castle to hear, let alone her husband next door. "Now ride the pony until I cum, damnit!!!! Work the spine out of my back. I'm going to drain every drop of Moët out of your chocolate bottle!"

And that's exactly what she proceeded to do, over and over and over again, leaving me walking with a limp to this day.

The woman broke into moves that I've only read about. Moves that made me forget that her husband was close by and scream — "Oh jeeeeeze, oh jeeeze, ooooh JEEEEEEEEEZE!!!!!" — in appreciation. Then I frigging lost it. Before I knew it, I was spurting the warm liquid into her and felt, too, her body lose itself in a sudden surge of heat.

Damn, as sore as I was, I had to get another round in just to pay her back. Then she had to pay me back, then I then she... I lost count of how many more.

"Black men never get it right," she complained when I couldn't take no more. "They think all they've got to do is produce a hard-on and then in and out. You'll be sorry later on in life if you can't learn to handle a woman proper. There's no telling how long that will take but just keep trying... It's not a man's prerogative to be satisfied, you know. You get yours, make sure she gets hers as well. That's the end of your session for today. *Next!* Just kidding..."

# PRE-COITAL

*There is much concern among the medical profession about the dramatic decline in male fertility in Western countries. Apparently one in six British couples now struggle to conceive and low male sperm count is the biggest reason.*

*The average man's sperm count has fallen by half in the last 60 years say experts. (Make's you wonder how they can cum up with such a figure don't it?)*

*In response, the Fertilisation and Embryology Authority, is allowing bulk imports of sperm from Denmark to address the acute shortage in the quality and quantity provided by British men for artificial insemination.*

*Just when you thought it couldn't get any worse for geezers comes another report from the 'Human Reproduction Journal' which shows that older men will find it more difficult to make a woman pregnant. After the age of twenty-four the chances decline by 3 per cent a year.*

*However low, every sperm counts.The paradox of our time*

*is that we spend more, but have less; we buy more, but enjoy it less; we've learned how to make a living, but not a life; nice houses, but broken homes; low sperm counts but more kids. These are times to stop and wonder, 'why'?*

I have a suspicion that it might come as a bit of an ego blow for us guys, but a recent survey of British women discovered that most of them find the average English geezer a complete bore (no pun intended) when it comes to the bedroom business. The report into sex secrets shows that compared to their counterparts in the United States, Australia or New Zealand, Brit birds are the most liberal-minded but most disappointed with the performance of their male country folk. Brit boys are called 'unadventurous' and 'ill-informed' about how to satisfy them. Two thirds of women questioned said they fake orgasms.

From what I've heard from many women, the reason a lot of guys are not too hot when it comes to playing the bedroom bully, is because they give it too much 'wham bam' and not enough creative interpretation. But then again, we are talking about women here and, as we men know only too well, no matter how much you do some women are never satisfied.

As for Lady P, I never had any trouble sleeping after

my night with her. Like I never had anything to be worried about, despite having just bonked my host's wife in his own castle. Even now it scares me that I never seemed to allow the possibility of him slipping in during the night and murdering me in my sleep to weigh on my mind. My conscience is like that — stays quiet where a hard-on's involved.

That night, I dreamt that I became a woman. In fact, it was a nightmare, but at least I got to find out all the reasons why it's great being a man:

- You don't have to shave below your neck.

- You can open all your own jam jars.

- Chocolate is just another snack and, sometimes, a meal in itself.

- The same hair style lasts for years, sometimes decades.

- Reverse parking is easy.

- Queues for public toilets don't exist, and you can go without a support group.

- Sex means never having to worry about your

reputation, and all your orgasms are real.

•Foreplay is optional.

•Biological clock? What's that?

•If you're thirty-four and single nobody notices.

•Window shopping is what you do when you buy windows.

•You never feel compelled to stop a spar from getting laid. In fact you encourage him.

•Not liking a person doesn't exclude having great sex with him.

•Same work, more pay...

I was awoken to the slam of the door to the en suite and the sound of water gushing through the shower. Where am I? What happened? I lay staring at the ceiling. Most of the previous night seemed a blur. Slowly I remembered. I remembered kicking it with her ladyship the whole night.

Lady P hadn't intended to stay the night. We must have fallen asleep.

*Why'd she leave that money on the dresser for me?*

I looked up as Lady P came out of the bathroom with a towel around her.

"Breakfast is downstairs in fifteen minutes."

"What time is it?" I asked sleepily.

"Quarter to eight," she said with a smile, a wink and a disappearance. How come I'm thinking about sex again? Does it really never leave my mind?

Naked and alone, I got up slowly and went into the en suite, locked the door behind me. Lost in thought, I took a long hard look at my shagged out features in the mirror above the wash basin. "Something has gotta give." All this hardcore bumping and grinding was doing me in. All this two hours of sleep business was killing me. Now that I had seen how the other half screw, maybe I needed to take a sabbatical from naked women. I mean, the mind is as strong as you allow it to be.

*Penis control, penis control, penis control…*

It is amazing how I already feel better for chanting that — physically, mentally and spiritually. Now that I have it out of my system, perhaps I won't think about sex for about another thirty seconds so I can get some work done. Maybe if I trained as a Shaolin monk…

Like someone once said, 'the man who straddles the

fence castrates his own self'. When his lordship joined me and his missus for breakfast downstairs, he looked like a man who had lost his bollocks.

Immaculately dressed in a tweed suit, he was in his early to mid fifties, with thinning grey hair, rosy red cheeks and the obligatory stiff upper lip. Too much booze and too many late nights had given him a kind of haggard look.

When I introduced myself, he glared at me like he wanted to thrust a dagger between my shoulder blades, like he was thinking, 'Why did my wife consort with this bloke?' Apart from that he ignored me, making the situation even more awkward.

He turned to his wife. "What's made you feel so good today? I haven't seen you smile for at least two weeks."

"Nothing."

"It must be something, darling. There must be a reason."

She got up and walked over to the window overlooking their vast acreage. He looked at her as she moved. Her tight skirt hugged her buttocks. Could it be, I wondered, that his lordship was thinking what I was thinking? I continued tucking into my pancakes and eggs, like I was invisible.

"What a night we had last night. We didn't get to bed until around four or five."

"So I heard," his lordship snapped.

"Yeah man," her ladyship stressed, sounding real ghetto.

"So this is your new boy?" he said, his hands on his hips.

"Why, are you jealous?"

His lordship pointed his butter knife at me.

"You... whoever you are... you're nothing," he said. "She's a whore, you're just insignificant."

Before he could say another word, she reached out and boxed the taste out of his mouth.

"Look who's talking about whore. That's a laugh. Listen," she continued, "I warned you when you were sleeping around that you better cut that out or you're going to be sorry. 'Don't do it, you'll regret it,' I said. But you wouldn't listen because you don't respect me. You want to play ruff — fine."

"Well... I am sorry."

"Sorry for what?"

"Sorry for sleeping around."

She boxed him again. This time harder.

"...and sorry for calling you a whore."

I didn't want to get caught in the crossfire so I ducked under the dining table (you'd think I would have done this before, but it was new to me).

It must be hard trying to maintain a stiff upper lip when your wife's sleeping with the man who has just eaten out of your refrigerator. That's always the way isn't it. The guy who's getting off with your wife is someone you know — a guest, sometimes even your best friend. It crosses every father's mind at some time or other that his kids might really belong to one of his mates. Society doesn't want to contemplate it. Think of the reverberations. We'd have men everywhere with no friends, and no doubt a lot of mothers would be embarrassed.

Take this bloke I know (I have to be a little diplomatic here so as to not identify the person in question), he has a 'friend' who is married, but the husband is living in Jamaica. Now this woman has a lover over here and has become pregnant. Not wanting to have a child or an abortion she has decided to go to Jamaica, sleep with the husband, tell him she is pregnant by him and offload the child on him before skipping back to Britain. I mean, dark or what? Maybe I'm too sensitive for this hard world, but stuff like that makes me think twice about ever having sex. I wonder what makes a woman act like that? Beats me how Terry can even go along with it, that's his child. He has to live with someone else bringing up his child for the rest of his life.

Back under the table, I could feel perspiration

running down the inside of my arms as his lordship's thoughts switched to me. Why oh why didn't I leave the man's missus alone?

"How could you... with *him?*" he says, but he really doesn't want to know.

"Like you're such a diamond geezer! What about all the men you've been sleeping with?"

*WHAT??!*

What did she know about me, he asked.

"He was hitch-hiking."

"He's a vagabond and you brought him here. Are you out of your mind, woman?"

*Wait a second, slow down, you're losing me. Let's get back to the bit about his lordship's sexual orientation.*

I have wondered many times on the reasoning behind 'straight' people marrying someone who is 'gay'. I guess some people enjoy threesomes, but why get married? Why not just keep swinging and leave marriage out of it? And why tell an eighteen year old hitch hiker that your husband is having an affair with another woman, when he's having an affair with another man?

Lady P might be a damn liar, but she certainly knew her husband. Because what seemed to hurt him the most was that she had slept with the 'enemy'. He too held brothas responsible for everything. He more or less said that a black man shot JFK, started WW2, was at the controls of the Titanic, and that the Black Death was so named because a black man must have had something to do with it. "And what's more, they don't do oral." He reminded her that black men were the cause of her unhappiness when he picked her up out of the Brixton ghetto and took her up-market. I don't know if it was his insecurity or what, but he felt the need to add that white men treat black women better.

He's not alone in thinking that he is doing black womanhood a favour. Just check out some of the personal ads from white guys in black newspapers. They often stress words like, 'well-off' or 'knows how to treat a woman like a lady' in the belief that these will be a novelty to black women and, therefore, some unique selling point. Yeah, *right*.

I get the same vibe from some white women checking black guys. They have this belief that they are superior goods and that their partner is with them because he's not too impressed with the sistas. I don't know if it's some innate sense of smug superiority, that too many Europeans are conditioned into believing, or insecurity but, whatever the reason, the attitude is too common for my liking.

"Darling, let's make love now," Lady P suggested suddenly. "Maybe I'll get pregnant today. I just feel it."

"What, right here? In broad daylight?"

"Oh darling," she said, hitching up her tartan skirt, "maybe that's the trouble. You only like to make love in the dark. Perhaps if we did it in the light for a change something might happen."

Life is weird. A woman can be nice to you one minute, and not give a damn about you the next. Only a woman can cuss a man out, make him feel like doo-doo then make love to him and make him feel like a king. Women are men without the bollocks. Just like men, they are capable of anything.

Lady P no longer had any use for me, that much was clear. I know you want all the sordid details and, ordinarily, I would get into it, but this was just too dirty in my opinion. It was horrible. Nasty. I mean, downright *nasty*, especially looking at it from under the table. I'm telling you, it felt weird. But at least now I know I'm not the only guy who goes cross-eyed during intercourse.

Yeah, I know, I've got a weird sense of humour. There's just some things that have me laughing my head off that may not be appropriate to laugh about at a certain moment. For example, even though it wasn't funny at the time, those smelly little toes always bring a smile to my face.

For a gay man in a marriage of convenience, his

lordship did have some moves, though. Watching them on the job was like Monday Night RAW. And another thing, I don't believe for one minute that that was his real phallus — the one he was born with. That stuff must have been enhanced, I'm telling you. The things they can do with a little surgery nowadays. Trust me, his Lordship had the biggest, meanest beast I had ever seen in my life, and that is more than a black man can chew.

I haven't seen Miss P since then. I regret not parting company amicably. I asked her when I should call her, she replied "How about never?"

# BEWARE A KNIGHT IN SHINING AMOUR

*Q: How many honest, intelligent, caring men in the world does it take to do the dishes?*
*A: Both of them.*

*Q: Why don't women blink during foreplay?*
*A: They don't have time.*

*Q: What do you call a woman who knows where her husband is every night?*
*A: A widow.*

*Q: Why are married women heavier than single women?*
*A: Single women come home, see what's in the fridge and go to bed. Married women come home, see what's in bed and go to the fridge.*

*Q: What is the one thing that all men at singles bars have in common?*
*A: They're married.*

*Q: If they can put a man on the moon — why don't they put them all up there?*

*Q: What's the difference between one man and the next?*
*A: Men are all the same. They just have different faces so that you can tell them apart.*

*Q: What's the definition of a bachelor?*
*A: A man who has missed the opportunity to make some woman miserable.*

*Q: Do women always have to make fools of men?*
*A: No. Most of them are the do-it-yourself types.*

I don't know if it's some innate secret desire among a lot of women to be treated like a slut in the bedroom, but the bedroom bullies with gold or plat fronts always seem to get the gals. As I've said before, nice guys cum (sic) last, but a fat lot of thanks we get for it. But if you're thugged out, over six feet, look like Tyson's brother and drive something with at least three 'r's in its badge name, a lot of women will consider you 'interesting'. Part of the female persona is that of reformer. A man enters a relationship hoping that the woman won't change. A woman on the other hand enters with the belief that she can change the man. Reforming a rogue is a challenge many women seem so keen to enter into.

Ladies, don't get me wrong. I know women aren't entirely to blame. There are some guys out there who could do with a lesson in mass debate.

Women might be able to fake orgasms, but men can fake whole relationships. Take the case of Diane who, for ten months, believed she was in the relationship that was going to last a lifetime. Such was the extent of her flight of fancy that she often used to take a ten-minute detour so as to pass the bridal wear shop on her way home from work.

As she would drone on and on about how wonderful this guy was, I'd pretend like I was was interested and occasionally asked the obvious like: "So Diane, if he really works as an investment broker how come he always asks you to pay when you go out?" I tried telling her that ten months was early days yet, but she didn't want to hear.

Of course, the inevitable happened. One day she discovers that her bank account and credit card statements have had more entries than a porn movie actress, and darling Basil has gone AWOL with her Saab cabriolet. To this day she hasn't seen her car or that waster. I told her to report the matter to the police but like a fool she actually believed a letter he left behind at her flat saying he was suffering from stress. That was four months ago and I'm sure she still thinks that he'll turn up tomorrow and say it's all been a bit of a misunderstanding.

Then there are those guys who regard baby fathering as an Olympic sport in which they intend to strut off with the gold. On my former road in the people's republic of Hackney, lives a 'man' who has 24 children with 19 different women. The honest fact of the matter is that he's not even certain how many children he has, but his nearest estimate is "around 24".

Of course he doesn't see all these kids. In fact, there are only a few that he has any form of contact with. He is in his late thirties and now says he regrets his behaviour which was at its most extreme when he was in his early twenties. Like so many other stupid men he thought the mark of a 'real man', was a guy who could 'breed up' as many gals as possible.

There are plenty of bronze medalists in this game. Maturity in a man is, unfortunately, something that only usually comes very late in the day. There are many guys who, now in their thirties, forties and fifties, reflect back on some of the actions they took when they were many years younger. Indeed, a good friend of mine who has fathered eight children with five mothers, is now trying to make good the stupidity of his past. His justification for his earlier actions rest in his ranking dread beliefs that supported his deeds of going forth and multiplying.

He at least has seen the error of his ways and is trying to make the present and future a better place. In the last few years he has made sure that, for the first time, all his children know him, and know about the existence of their brothers and sisters.

There are too many wotless geezers in this world for my liking, especially when you're the father of a daughter who will be a teenager within ten years. It's the time every father dreads when in a few years his girl will be going out on dates. Where on earth will she find a husband who will love her, honour her, respect her, support her, cherish her, intellectualise with her, bring mirth to her, etc, etc? I mean, the standard has dropped considerably in the last few years. You hear about the problems many women say they have in finding Mr Write (and able to read). I'm told that there are women out there who demand that their man can both spell his own name and be able to have a conversation that involves a vocabulary of more than seven words.

Then there are those blokes who won't take 'no' for an answer. A Turkish man whose marriage proposal was rejected by his intended bride's father, killed six members of her family before shooting himself in Germany recently.

It just goes to show that the father was absolutely right in refusing to have him as a son-in-law. There is an old Hungarian saying that states: 'Better to have your entire family horribly murdered by a psychotic madman than to have an in-law who will embarrass you at family gatherings.' It may be a long saying, but certainly one that is full of the wisdom that the Hungarians are so well-known for.

It does make you wonder what sort of geezer goes along to dad to ask for permission to marry his daughter, and decides to take a big f**k-off handgun with him. I mean what goes through your head at such moments? "Oh, I must ask for my darling Inga's hand in marriage, but let me take my Browning Hi-Power along in case there is some dispute about how many tiers there are going to be on the wedding cake."

Personally speaking, the idea of having to resort to a gun seems unimaginable. If I had some rhatid big automatic weapon, I don't see how I'd need to ask anyone's permission for marriage. The only time I could have imagined a firearm and wedding going together was the possibility of some irate father marching me up the aisle with a shotgun after getting his virginal daughter in the family way.

Okay, I can understand that no one likes rejection and Mustafa might have felt like the old man needed a good kicking for being a smug git, but was it necessary to wipe out the whole family?

"So, laughing grandma, you think it funny that I should want to marry Inga? Well, take that…"

*Boom!*

"And you, Auntie, you never really did like my dress sense did you? Well, take that…"

*Boom!*

"As for you, uncle, you always took the piss out of the old Skoda I drive…"

*Boom!*

The mind boggles at how some folk stay.

Thirty years ago I can remember a Sunday when I was dragged off to church to hear some minister wail on about the evil ways of the world and how judgement day was just around the corner. Of course we had to wait another 25 years before *Judgement Day* did finally arrive, but it was worth it. Definitely one of the best Arnie films, that's for sure. But anyway, I digress. One thing I can remember the minister banging on about was the decline in the traditional family and how this was destroying the fabric of society. Of course when you're eight or nine you're not really too concerned about the future of the family. The graphic descriptions of Sodom were a great deal more interesting to me, but maybe we shouldn't go there for the moment. Anyway, let's fast forward and survey the landscape today. Had the minister been sampling too much of the communion wine or was he a bit of a sage?

It's only when a man has a daughter that he fully realises the meaning of the word 'family' and the need for men to start taking their child rearing responsibilities seriously. There are implications about this whole dip and chip mentality that some guys possess, that is likely to have worrying implications for the future.

The saying, 'the chickens have come home to roost', may start to take on a particular significance for those geezers who have bred children by an assortment of baby mothers and not stayed around long enough to even know the youts' names.

I was given reason to reflect on the consequences of the hit and run Mr Lovermen by a friend's sister. The woman in question has a son by a man who made a mad dash for the door when he discovered that the stork was about to pay a visit.

The young boy, now thirteen, recently met a similar aged girl and the two of them were getting on like Romeo and Juliet. That is until they realised they shared something in common — the same dad! Fortunately the truth came out before things had gone too far down the line, but both were left very upset by the whole business and it didn't do their self-esteem any good.

The boy's mother knew nothing about the family connection and, indeed, now realises that she hasn't a clue how many other half-sisters and brothers might be out there waiting to bump into her son at some future date.

So how many kids could this man have brought into the world? Only God knows. Many of the offspring of these 'performers' are now of an age where they are starting to form relationships with the opposite gender. How many of them will have the misfortune to go through what my friend's nephew went through?

And if you've ever been the victim of sperm banditry, you'll know that the world is a very small place. Too small. Of course, it's not just this current generation of reckless, selfish and irresponsible geezers who need to make sure that those chickens coming home to roost aren't about to settle on their fence. It's us innocent guys, too.

Call me over-protective, too picky, too choosy, but I'm not taking any chances. As soon as any boy/man should so much as say 'hello' to my daughters, he'll be given one of the following application forms which I've devised.

I would advise any concerned father to plan ahead and get some of these printed. If nothing else, you'll soon know if the guy can at least write. Be very wary of anyone who completes the form in green crayon!

*Note: This application will be incomplete and rejected unless accompanied by a complete financial statement, job history, lineage, and current medical report from your doctor.*

1.    What is your name, age, NI number, and IQ?

_____

2.    Do you have one male and one female parent?

_____

If "No", explain:

_____

3. Do you own or have access to a van?

_____

4.Do you own or have access to a car with dark tinted windows?

_____

5. Do you own or have access to a waterbed?

_____

6. Do you have an earring, nose ring, or nipple ring?

_____

7. Do you have a tattoo?

_____

*(If you have answered YES to #3, #4 or #5, discontinue application and leave the premises immediately.)

8.    In fifty words or less, what does 'LATE' or 'SOON REACH' mean to you?

_____

9.    In fifty words or less, what does 'DON'T TOUCH MY DAUGHTER' mean to you?

_____

10.  In fifty words or less, what does 'ABSTINENCE' mean to you?

_____


11.  In fifty words or less, what does 'SERIOUS PAIN' mean to you?

_____


12.  Which church do you attend?

_____


13.  How often do you attend?

_____


14.  When would be the best time to interview your mother, father and pastor?

_____


15.  Please fill in the blanks:

If I was shot, the last place on my body I would want wounded would be my

_____


If I took some blows, the last bone I would want broken would be my

_____

A woman's place is in the

_____

The one thing I hope this application doesn't ask is

_____

When I meet a girl, the one thing I always notice first is her

_____

*(Note: If answer to last question begins with "T" or "A", discontinue and leave premises immediately — keeping your head low.)*

16.    What do you want to be IF you grow up?

_____

I swear that all the above information is correct to the best of my knowledge under penalty of death, bodily harm, dismemberment, torture or mental abuse.

Signature of applicant

_____

Signature of father

_____

Signature of mother

_____

Signature of legal guardian

_____

Signature of pastor

_____

Signature of local MP

_____

*Thank you for your interest (it had better be genuine and non-sexual). Please allow 4-6 years for processing. You will be contacted in writing if approved. If denied, please never apply again. Don't call me, I'll call you.*

# WHAT HAVE YOU DONE FOR ME LATELY?

*The so-called professional, liberated woman wants to have her cake and eat it too. Some of them have gone to college and earned degrees. They have entered the work force and are attempting, even as we speak, to make an impact in corporate life and government. Today's woman wants liberation in her job. She wants equality in the classroom. She wants to do what she wants to do, when she wants to do it, with whom she wants to do it. She wants freedom. I have no problem with that. More power to her. But I ask one simple question: WHY ARE MEN STILL FOOTING THE BILL?*

Q: What do men and sperm have in common?
A: A one-in-a-million chance of becoming a human being.

   I'm not sure what I've done to offend anyone but last

week I got this anti-man 'joke' faxed to me with some some sort of accusation that me sexual practices were of a solo nature. Can't think I've said anything that could be rude to birds. Oh well, I guess it must be one of them cropped-haired, dungaree and Doc Marten boot-wearing feminist lesbian types I've heard about. Thank you whoever you are. We're all refreshed and challenged by your unique point of view.

It's not easy being a man these days. For years you exist in a comfortable double standards world, then along comes women who suddenly start to play men at their own game.

Take relationships, or more specifically sexual relationships. Every other woman describes herself as being single and saintly. However, if you dig a bit deeper below the surface and if folk were really honest, you discover that women who publicly describe themselves as undiscovered as the remote rainforests of Papua New Guinea, are in fact more like the Tottenham Court Road — everyone's been up there. Likewise guys who tell you that they are single, celibate and waiting for Ms Right, are either liars, have had their sexual organs removed following an industrial accident, or mentally deranged.

Q: Why is it difficult to find men who are sensitive,

**Annual Meeting of Single, Good looking, Straight, Emotionally-Stable, Financially-Secure, Intelligent Men Looking for a Long-Term Commitment**

caring and good looking?

A: They already have boyfriends.

Now I wouldn't for one moment say that the average 'single' man and woman out there are at it like hammer and nail, but the myth of the totally single woman is mainly that, a myth.

Just as a man needs his 'tings' so too does a woman. Men call 'sex', but women call it 'sensuality'. Guys want it hard and strong whereas most women prefer it hard and long. But both male and female thrive on it. The difference is that women tend to be a whole heap more discreet about it. Don't be fooled for one moment into thinking that all these single women are sitting at home of an evening reading their Bible, sewing, and waiting for Mr Right. More often than not, while holding on for Mr Right they are having fun with Mr Wrong (or, if you're Chinese, Mr Wong!)

Traditionally it was us guys who had 'x amount' of booty calls listed in our Nokia, but women can now play that game too, and a lot of guys aren't feeling too comfortable about it. I overheard one guy chatting to his spar on the 73 bus the other day and I had to smile. Says brothaman: "Nah, I don't go around there no more for no booty call. The woman just wants me for sex. I don't like being used."

God bless us. Only a man could hold such illogical and unfair double standards yet totally believe his case to be just and self-evident. His spar was nodding his understanding of the guy's dilemma and punctuating it with a very definite "Seen, seen," so he too must empathise with the dude's plight.

In the old days, a woman wanted her tings but played a game of NOT telling her squeeze that his only real use was to rock her bed posts, not her world. Men's egos were protected and the world was a happier and safer place. What of course is happening now is that women can't be arsed with all the bollocks and are just saying like it is.

One mate of mine told me almost in tears how a woman he had just met told him in no uncertain terms that he was just "a good f\*\*k" and that's all she wanted from him. It was how he saw her, too, but he said he felt crushed when she spelt it out in such blunt terms. He also didn't like the fact that if she had an orgasm before him she'd roll over, say "Show's over" and start to snore, but that is another story.

Men invented the booty call and even if we didn't, we'd like to think that we did. So why are we getting mad because women have mastered the game and are beating us at it? Why is it that we are surprised when certain women break up with us that they have a new boyfriend an hour later?

There may have been big changes in society, but the average man has not reached a point where he can feel totally happy about a woman asserting her sexuality and sexual needs in the same way that he does. The problem is that it's happening and there doesn't seem to be much that we can do about it.

T'ings ain't the things they used to be and it's not easy for us guys to adapt. As the man said "I've seen the future and it hurts". I guess we'll just have to learn to live with the pain.

I recently got dragged along to some kind of alpha male bonding group meeting where I came across some of the most pathetic whining whingers it's been my misfortune to meet. I know that these sorts of 'men bonding' things are popular these days but if this is some sort of indication of what the rest are like, please pass me the sick bag.

After hugging each other and shedding a few tears, the guys started sharing their stories:

"My boss's wife nicked my sperm. She used me as if I had 'sperm bank' written on my forehead. What the hell do I look like, a drive-through? Pull up, load up and keep going. I have had thirty-five different partners. I mean, I like to flirt — who doesn't. It sounds like fun and excitement to some people but I have now paid the price for it. I thought it was love she wanted. It never occurred to me that she might be sleeping with me to get pregnant. I've never thought of my sperm as valuable. Most of it goes to waste and there's plenty more where it came from — easy cum, easy go. Then she decides to get rid of it at the last minute. How come a woman can abort an unwanted child but a man in the same situation is required to pay years of child support? If a man wants her to have an abortion, that's an option solely within the control of the woman. If he doesn't want her to abort, that's an option solely within the control of the woman."

After listening to the little man blowing off steam, the next guy to speak came from a different angle:

"That subject's as worn out as Joan Collins's panty elastic and about as valid as Del Boy's MOT certificate. I really am tired of this blame the woman excuse. Most women think we're stupid. Hell, sometimes I think *we* think we're stupid. If you're a man, then act like one. Too bad we think acting like a man is sleeping with anything that moves. We've got to talk about penis control, because that's what's responsible for all our problems. How can we say on one hand we need women, we need the emotional contact, we need to feel like head of households, we need to feel appreciated, then say we're genetically engineered to spill as much seed as possible so therefore we will approach reproductive matters by leaving all the options with the woman? We pick and choose when we want to be men. When it's easier for us to be little boys we're little boys, when it's easier to be men we choose that. Fellas, it's time to realise that we are ALL responsible for what we do — unless we are celebrities."

The third guy to speak rejected this thesis:

"Just because men want to pursue women all the time, watch *Top Gear*, and think that a 'wife' is someone who cooks, doesn't mean we are immature and lack commitment."

The next guy added:

"Some people are sun worshippers, we are sex worshippers. By the way, anyone here know why some penises are crooked?"

T'ings ain't easy when you're the last caveman in town. If you've been brought up with certain attitudes it is not always easy to leave them behind. But there is a lot to be said for traditional caveman values. I see it as a getting back to basics philosophy. Needs are kept simple and to a minimum. Whereas most women will have a list of criteria longer than a supertanker, caveman's needs are simple. A philosophy of life which believes that breast size is more important than personality or that actually liking someone should not be an impediment to having sex with them, has much going for it.

No, it is not easy being a man these days. Every time you think you've got it good, someone just has to spit in your Ovaltine. For years you exist in the comfortable world of ignorance, then through your letterbox comes a letter from the Child Support Agency, claiming back-dated maintenance of £18,680 for a four-year-old child I've never heard of. I mean, who is Junior Marvin Braithwaite? There's gotta be some mistake. Sumt'ing nah *h*add up.

# LOVE WIZARD

*If you happen to be an ugly geezer it's probably better that you quietly slip off somewhere and end your sad and miserable existence now. It's not a good time for hugly folks says a new report from the Florida Atlantic University. The profs found that women who consider their partners good looking have more orgasms and better sex than those who found their partners average looking.*

*Having good looks will not only make you more of a bedroom thriller but it will also make you a boardroom killer. Or so teenagers think. A survey by Neutrogena recently discovered that teens rated looks more important than talent or intelligence in getting up the career ladder.*

*Of course, thanks to the Net, we can all be beautiful when we want to be.*

You're a woman who's just gone out on a date with this nice guy you met at the supermarket. What is the question your girlfriends are all going to ask you? Oh yes, that time honoured favourite of, "What's he do for a living?" Or to cut to the bottom line: "How much money does he earn and is he worth dropping the panties for?"

It doesn't matter how unattractive that fool is, how bad his breath or dress sense is, he can have the social graces of Ghengis Khan and the brains of a banana. But let my man be rolling in the holding-folding and I can bet your big ass dollar that Mr Fright will be pulling more crackers than the whole town on Christmas Day.

Every guy has looked at a criss gal on the arms of something that was at the bottom rung of Darwin's evolution chart, and wondered to himself, 'What has he got that I ain't got?' At least five noughts after the first digit of his salary cheque, dummy. That's what he's got.

So you think I'm exaggerating? Well how the hell do you think someone as ugly as Mike Tyson could ever get the babes he pulls? When Tyson fell out of the ugly tree, that sucker hit every damn branch! I can quite confidently say these things because (a) Mr Tyson doesn't visit Hackney that often and (b) Even someone that ugly must own a mirror in his yard.

But I digress. No, seriously, if further proof is needed, check out the findings of a recent survey conducted by researchers at the University of California, Los Angeles (UCLA). The survey of 3,407 single men and women aged between 18 to 55, revealed that for women, a man's income potential was more important than his physical attractiveness, education or occupation.

These academics need to seriously question where they keep their brains. These plonkers wasted goodness knows how much time and dollars interviewing thousands of people to come up with results I could have told them for nothing! One phone call is all it would have taken. They could have checked my digits with directory enquiries but no, they've got to go and discover the blindingly obvious for themselves.

Ever since the first man built up a fine designer cave and realised that, as a result, he had his pick of the nicest cave women, guys have known the score. The more the corn you hold, the bigger the choice when it comes to the ladies.

In turn, women have known that all they have to do to pull Mr Right was to look good and dress nice. Indeed the UCLA survey found that men place most emphasis on physical beauty when it comes to choosing a partner than on anything else. Guy's just aren't too deep I'm afraid. Good chest, nice backside, pretty face, is the sophisticated criteria most guys use in the selection process.

However, the times they are a-changing! Going back again to this UCLA survey, one important factor that the researchers found was that a growing number of men are going out with a woman because of how much money *she* earns. The study shows that men are now placing a potential wife's income as more important than her age, race or religion. The study sheds new light on the value that men are starting to place on women's economic status and earning potential.

"We might expect women to consider a man's earning potential but not men," explains UCLA psychologist Belinda Tucker. "This reflects the new reality for men. Making it today often requires two income-producing partners."

I think Ms Tucker has hit the nail squarely on its head. A few years back many guys I knew just checked a woman for her crissness, now many of these same blokes are not into a nice behind, but more concerned with a woman's assets. The reality is that as time goes by even the most hardened player starts to realise that gal fitness is not going to pay the mortgage. What job your potential missus does is going to determine what kind of lifestyle you're going to have together.

# BONKERS

## EXCLUSIVE

### Lad seduced at 15

### by mum, 30, faces

### £55,000 CSA bill

Furious . . . John Walker

**By JOHN SCOTT**

A PLUMBER seduced by a woman when he was just 15 is facing a £55,000 maintenance bill for a child he never knew he had.

Stunned John Walker, now 25, is being pursued for cash by the Child Support Agency.

*He is furious at being asked to pay when the woman – who was twice his age – broke the law by bonking him when he was under age.*

John, of Birmingham, said: "I thought the dream of every lad had come true. I didn't know it was going to turn into such a nightmare."

*Full Story – Page Nine*

I recently saw my spar go ga-ga for a woman who I thought wasn't right for him. He just met the gal and was already booking the church for the big day. Then disaster struck. He found he couldn't get on with her. He had got so caught up in fantasising about the suburban dream home that their joint incomes could buy as a married couple that he became blind to the reality.

But he's not the only guy just looking at the dollars. A woman friend of mine has just blown her savings on a seriously wicked looking Beamer convertible. The reaction from guys has been crazy, she says. Men are now coming up to her and asking her out all the time because they think she is in some well-paid, high-flying job.

As I said, the times they are a-changing. Man is no longer the hunter and the provider while the good woman stays at home and skins the dead woolly mammoth. The roles of provider are being more evenly split between man and woman. At the end of the day that must be a good thing. One day, maybe a woman may even take me out for dinner and actually pay for the meal!

# IF YOU NEED THE DISHES DONE...

*'Well, well, well, that's hardly a surprise' is my thoughts about the new report which says that despite the much hyped image of the new man, the average geezer hasn't got any enthusiasm for housework and, in fact, does very little of it.*

*Quite frankly, the whole crap trap about the new man in the new millennium is about as convincing to me as when Bill Clinton said he smoked a spliff but didn't inhale. I never bought the idea of this caring, sharing guy who changes the nappies and runs about in a pinny cleaning up the home.*

*The survey, published by Home-To-Home magazine, found that 87% of women change the beds compared with only 4% of men (the other 9% of households are presumably students and single men whose beds never get made). In fact most of the tedious and boring household chores are, in the main, still done by women. Feminists like Germaine Greer will say that women are getting a bad deal etc etc. Fair enough. Even an old* unreconstructed pig like me can't expect in this day and age for a woman to act as some sort of unpaid scivvy in a relationship, so I won't condone men who don't do their fair share. But the fact of the matter is that women love all that household business. In fact women are better designed to do simple and repetitive tasks. It's a scientific fact.

Why do you think that 99.9999% of men get hitched in the first place? It isn't for the unlimited sex on tap. In this day and age there is 'nuff of that going around that you don't need a certificate and reception for 200 guests to get some. Companionship? No, a man can buy a cat if he needs a companion. Someone to talk to? Don't be silly. The average married man will be lucky if he gets more than five words in edgeways during the average conversation with his other half.

Those wannabe new men who raise women's hopes with all this talk about sharing women's jobs, really deserve a good kicking. Men like that have got a lot to answer for. Imagine the trouble they have caused us ordinary guys with all this talk of equality on the domestic front. Please note, there will never be equality in the home because men and women are different.

It's a scientific fact that men are better at handling power tools than women, so we'll always be better at drilling holes in walls. If you need a hole in a wall in your home, then as far as I'm concerned, I'm your man. But if it's washing up that needs sorting, then it's the woman that is more able to deal with such a job. It's just scientific, innit.

Women have had millions of years to develop domestic skills such as dusting, washing, cooking etc. During the same period of time, men have developed talents in other departments. Skills in building pyramids, hunting wild bears, archery and operating power tools have been passed onto us by our fathers over centuries, so it makes sense that men use the skills that they have.

If the lion is good at killing things and a giraffe is good at looking over high walls, doesn't it make sense that, should you need a killing thing or a high thing, you would use the appropriate animal for the task at hand. It's so scientific, innit.

My missus says that women who aspire to be the equal of men lack ambition. I don't know what she means by that exactly but I'm sure it endorses my views that men and power tools do mix, and that Marigold don't make washing up gloves to fit our big hands.

Braithwaite? *Braithwaite…* Now you mention it, that name does ring a bell. I can only think of one person I've been with who had that name. But I didn't have sex with her. Did I?

*Dear CSA*
*'…lemme see his hands.'*
*yours sincerely*
*D*

Tonya Braithwaite is a gal I met in church, at a funeral,
about five years ago. Just before I met Sweetie (this was
the said period in my life when I just didn't care and
wasn't too picky about who I was sleeping with and lost
count). Looking at her, there was no indication that
things would turn out the way they eventually did.

"Why are you looking at my rear end?" she said,
turning suddenly.

I should have been honest and said, ' 'Cause I want to
get a good look at what I'm going to be dealing with
later.' But that would have seemed like wishful thinking.
So I lied and said I was an artist and was wondering
whether she would pose naked for me — in the name of
art.

She laughed that dismissive laugh of hers and said,
"Sounds like a pimp's best recruiting line."

But after a few minutes she said, "Yes." Said there was
something about me that made her feel she could trust
me, something in my smile that was 'drawing' her
towards me.

I thought nothing of it when she invited me around to
her house for the first sitting, and told me to bring my
toolbox. Indeed I replied that I never leave home
without it.

I mean, how could I have guessed that her main reason for attending the funeral was to find a man? That's right, she was out on the pull. Not looking for a man with money, but one who possessed a multitude of DIY skills, because she needed some shelves putting up and some other bits and bobs sorted out.

So I went round to Tonya's beech laminated, lime-green, brush chromed, micro hi-fied, dream home in Harlesden.

Tonya was a real ghetto gal, one of those super women who give the impression that they like to be able to wear something that resembles trousers around the house and can function totally fine on their own even if some wotless baby father should leave them stranded with ten kids and no money. This age old vision of the strong woman who is capable of doing everything from three jobs on her own to repairing a thermo nuclear engine without the need for no man, makes guys feel that women haven't really got a need, so we haven't got a role to play, and if we haven't got a role we don't really need to have any responsibility. I wonder for example how many baby fathers would be more involved if these women actually went down on their knees and begged, "I REALLY need your help."

As soon as I got to her house Tonya told me what she

wanted and what she was offering in return. "Men are from Mars women are from venus... men are better with power tools and having a penis," she said in a reluctant admission of the superiority of the male.

At the funeral where we met, Tonya looked every bit Ms Prim and Proper in nothing but Harvey Nicks, but at home she turns into Tonyanisha — Ms Ghettofabulous in gold shorts filled with amazing legs and a bum that would make Stevie Wonder see. Waving the Black & Decker in my hand, I complimented her several times on how good she looked.

In this consumer obsessed society, it is a wonder that the average man can ever get laid without having to risk their manhoods with equipment as deadly as a loaded .357 Magnum. On that day at Tonya's house, with the jigsaw between my legs to cut a measure of shelving, I slipped and came dangerously close to discovering my feminine side. My whole sex life flashed before my eyes (actually it rolled on and on for about as long as an arty French film, but that's another story) as the blade headed for me wedding tackle. There for the grace of the willy fairy go I.

Honestly, I read a report last week that the number of DIY accidents is soaring. TV programmes and nagging girlfriends are driving men to take up the challenge of home 'improvement' with the sort of enthusiasm not seen since woodchip and louvre doors were the lick. The problem with these sorts of TV shows is that they make every DIY job look like a piece of piss when in reality it's not that easy. Believe me, jigsaws have a mind of their own and they never follow the line marked out in pencil.

How you train a power saw to follow a pencil line is a mystery to me and most blokes. Like a 14 stone Great Dane, you let it off the leash and hope that it will go in the general direction that you want it to go.

When a woman's sexual favours are traded against home improvements you can bet that it's got to be a deal where the geezer comes second, minus a hand or with a staple moving around his bloodstream. It's only then that he realises that the only safe DIY is done in the privacy of your own home and with a thumbed copy of *Readers Wives*.

Tonya wanted a designer look to her home and a whole kitchen unit installed but would settle for the shelves for now. She was willing to make it worth my while.

"I'll have something cooking for you when you're done," she promised, with more than a hint of a blowjob in her eye.

Men are too stupid and women too clever. I mean, what does 'something cooking' actually mean? Maybe if

I had thought less about the 'heaven' between her thighs I would have got her to sign a contract stating what exactly I was going to get for my DIY skills. I didn't pay it any attention because I couldn't see past my penis. I had made a mental decision not to suppress my want/urge/need. I was too busy fantasising, aching to get with her, daydreaming about it. Trying to get these shelves up quick time.

Got to stop thinking about the *putang* so much though. That stuff is like my kryptonite. I've got nothing but *putang* on the brain it seems.

So when the shelves were up and it was time to get paid, she took me by the hand to her bedroom and told me to lie down on her bed.

I did as I was ordered. She stripped down to her bikini thingy, putting temptation before me. My groin started twitching and my pulse went into overdrive. The inside of my thighs quivered. The voice in my ear kept saying, *You lucky bastard, you're going to get your rocks off before I count to ten.*

But if I thought that I would get my groove on, I was mistaken.

"Are you trying to have sex with me?" she enquired as I went up behind her and slipped one hand on the behind I had had my mind on since I first set eyes on it.

"If so, I'd rather be just good friends."

"It's not about sex," I lied. "It's about you and me...
the stars and the moon, the birds and the bees. It's about
those shelves I've put up. It's about life, y'know, Tee."

"If it isn't about sex then keep your *dayum* hands off
me..."

She withdrew my hand for me.

"Excuse me as I get real for a minute, but I thought we
had a deal. Pray explain the change in circumstance," I
protested. "Sex, that's the deal isn't it? What happened
to my blowjob?"

"Blowjob? No, I don't think so. There was no hint of a
blowjob or anything else. I said 'I'll have something
cooking for you' and I have..."

With that she proceeded to to take off her blouse.
Then she dropped her drawers. Then, mouth half-open,
she dropped to her knees, taking my zip down with her
and pulled out my treasures, like I was about to feel her
sensual pleasure, like she was going to suck the
sweetness as she would the filling in a Cadbury's creme
egg.

Wishful thinking.

Instead she proceeded to set my balls on fire by
gripping my shaft tightly with one hand and rubbing in
a violent pumping motion with quick up-and-down
strokes while pinching my crotch with the other hand

like I was a piece of meat.

I looked on, bewildered and appaled. It was kinda nice, if painful, but it wasn't what I came for. I can do that at home by myself on my own with no baggage and no regrets.

"Yankey doodle went to town riding on his pony," she hummed, "with his dickie in his hand because he's very horny."

"No more!'" I could feel myself cumming. But I didn't want to go out like that. I am too freaking young to be a tosser. I haven't got time for this when the world is full of pum.

But when a woman's determined to make a man cum, there's not much he can do to hold back.

"Ha-yah, ha-yah, ha-yah," was my war cry. "Ooooooweeee, baby, ooooweeee. No. No. No. Aaaaaaaah, yes, yes, yes... that's right, that's it..."

She smiled sweetly as I literally came in her hands.

"Is this it?" I gasped and panted, rubbing my nuts and stomach gently. "Aren't you even going to show me how deep you can go? Aren't you even going to make me beg for more?"

"You're too girlie-girlie, that's your problem, D."

"Girl, I don't know what kind of guys you are used to dating, but you're supposed to slob da knob, not scrub it up. It's not made of rubber, y'know, you can't buy this at Ann Summers in ninety-nine colours."

"You expect me to slobber all over your cock? Don't you even give a toss where my mouth has been?"

I shook my head. No I didn't.

"Men — you cant live without 'em, and you're not allowed to kill 'em... Do you even have any idea how many sex partners you have had?"

Why do so many women define a man by how many women he has slept with, or is in the process of baggin'?

"Damn, you know what, to be perfectly honest, I stopped counting at about three."

"Three! You've slept with three different women?!"

"Well, three women in the last four years. But I'm pretty young, I'll make up for it."

To be hung up on a number is stupid. There is no such thing as too much pum. And if that makes me a super slag, well, at least I'm good at something. I don't put somebody down or knock 'em for the number of people they have slept with. I judge a man by his mind-set and values. I tried to explain that to Tonya but she wouldn't listen.

"Three women!!! You may as well have tattooed across your forehead 'Hi, I'm D, I'm addicted to sex'," she exclaimed in horror. "And how many kids have you got out there? Do you even know?"

"No kids. Definitely. I'm 99.999999999999% sure that I don't have any kids out there."

"In other words, you're just not certain. No man is. Only a woman can be 100% sure."

"I said, I haven't got no kids…"

"You can believe whatever you want but you can't make me believe it!|"

She wasn't easy.

"Just chill," she told me as she started putting her clothes back on. "Try and control it. You're highly sexually charged. You're a dog. If I throw a stick, will you leave?"

"Aren't you horny too?"

"Not horny or stupid enough to let a man I hardly know have sex with me."

I shrugged my shoulders. Tonya got her shelves done. Then I got done. But it's like grandpa told me: "Women are just like colds. As soon as you get over one, you're bound to catch another one."

Nine months later I bumped into one of her girlfriends who had been at the funeral with her, and she informed me that Tonya had just given birth to a baby boy who she was raising together with her girlfriend.

*"Girlfriend?* There must be some mistake."

"No, no mistake, Tonya's been with her girlfriend at

their house in Harlesden for years now. They've been trying to have a baby for ages, but she finally found a suitable donor a while back."

At the time, the significance of the timing didn't alarm me. After all, we hadn't had sex. Had we? It's only now that I've got this bill from the CSA that I've started to think about it and wonder what was in her head when we parted company. Was she happy, overjoyed, or downright miserable? And what did she do with all that sperm she was holding?

# LESSONS IN LIFE

*A report by the Family Policy Studies Centre says that our society is producing fewer marriages and fewer kids in each marriage, but more divorces, more single parents and more people living on their own. In fact nearly 28% of homes are occupied by single people. That is three times as many as 40 years ago. Even more amazing is that almost a quarter of women born in 1973 are likely to be childless at the age of 45, compared to about one in 10 of those born in 1943.*

*Those women who are having children are having them later, on average at 29, and they are having fewer children. The average of 1.73 children per mother in the late 1990s may be higher than in other EU countries but is below the 2.1 needed to retain the population at its present level in the long term.*

It's not easy being a woman either.

"How come you don't you have any kids?" If you're a woman over thirty, it's the question that most adults wonder about?

It shouldn't be surprising that fewer women are having children. Kids equate to hard work, commitment and responsibility, and these facts of life don't sit comfortably with the young, free, and single lifestyle that more and more of us want to hang on to. Children are seen as obstacles in the way of making dollars and living the dream lifestyle. Yet women keep having them.

About 80% of my female friends in their thirties complain that they are childless and a large percentage of them look set to stay that way. Why? Because they have given up hope. The hope of finding the right or an all right man, and the hope that things will turn out fine in the long term. At the weekend one friend was telling me that she doesn't think she can love a man again and has resigned herself to being single for the rest of her life. *Rhatid!* The woman is only thirty-two for gawd sake. How the hell can you be having an attitude like this when you've probably got a least another forty years of living ahead?

Unfortunately it seems to be around the early thirties that the rot starts to set in. Optimism gives way to a slow pessimism that grows to outright cynicism. She slowly stops making an effort, the weight starts to pile on, the heart grows cold and more bitter.

My TV presenter friend who is in her late thirties told me recently that the topic comes up so often from her family that she feels almost apologetic about her lack of offspring.

One woman I used to work with, who is childless, said that her mum was practically in tears recently because she is having baby cravings and was worried that she will die without having any grandchildren. Poor mum is so desperate that she said to daughter, "Can't you just find some man somewhere to give you a child?"

Children are such a major part of life that a childless woman is viewed as peculiar. Some guys even feel that if a woman isn't pushing a pram she's probably a lesbo. When she gets into her mid-thirties the pressure grows even more intense. In the white world, a childless woman is often seen as someone focused on her career or wishing to live a particular lifestyle, but black women in a similar situation are more likely to be viewed with deep suspicion.

Personally, I can't see what the big fuss is all about. The M25 is at gridlock, you can't move down Oxford Street, and try and get a seat in a bar on a Friday night... The world is too bloody crowded already, so why the hell should we be concerned about something that can only make the problem of over-crowding worse?

Considering the fact that the word 'child' usually holds as much terror for men as do 'yours' and 'CSA', it's odd that childless women say that the biggest pressures come from men.

One male acquaintance of mine once told me that he never bothered dating women who didn't have pickney because it meant that 'they weren't domesticated' and wouldn't know how to look after a man. He felt that until a woman had a child she wouldn't know how to put someone first before herself.

A selfish git he may be, but this guy may have had a point. If you've never had to make compromises or self sacrifices to bring up a pickney then you're probably not willing to be selfless in a relationship.

Another male acquaintance of mine told me that he never dated women who didn't have pickney because it meant that they were always on the hunt for a father to their child. In his experience childless women viewed every man as a potential sperm donor. When it came to women with children, he had a set of questions for them:

"So you say you have a daughter? How old is she? Is her father actively involved in her life? Is he actively involved in yours? I don't have a problem with children, but I do have a problem with exes who insist on being involved with the life of the mother. Please tell me that isn't your situation."

There is too much emphasis placed on women being mothers and not enough emphasis on men being husbands and fathers, so I don't for one moment think it's right that childless women should be made to seem like some sort of freaks because of that fact. I don't see that women who choose not to have a child because they haven't found Mr Right, should feel under any pressure to jump on the baby mother bandwagon. I've seen it happen too often where a desperate woman will bed some wotless idiot just to have a baby to keep the world from feeling sorry for her childless state.

To those women who haven't felt the need to have children just because society says you should, I say well done to you. Do what you want to do and don't let anyone tell you different.

However, countless women with a yen for a baby have used a man purportedly for sex, but really for procreation (his story). And countless other women have been "shocked" themselves when contraception fails (her story).

The truth is that so many women have toyed with the idea of becoming pregnant without checking with the man first, we all know some. It could be because they have felt the pressure of the biological deadline. Sometimes it's to tie a man more securely. Usually it's simply because they want a baby. It doesn't matter what happens afterwards. They feel they're not quite legit until they have a kid.

One woman I used to know was dumped at the fag-end of a turbulent six year relationship that robbed her of the 'best years' of her life. She was thirty-seven with no man and no child and no plans for the future. Her face turned hard and her thoughts evil. "I am a woman of the twenty-first century, I don't need a man," she would say.

Amongst her friends, she denied that she still had it really bad for her ex. In fact, she went out of her way to show that she was sceptical of all guys now and that she had lost her faith in love too, so sex was all that was left. "The perfect man is a penis with a firm body,"she often quipped.

Yet she grabbed every opportunity that presented itself to diss her ex — "That raas is the most screwed-up man I have ever met. He thinks that he can just go around grinding everybody and then moving on... He's going to pay!"

When she bumped into her ex with his new beau at a cinema all hell broke lose. My friend lost it and grabbed her rival by the throat, screaming "You coolie bitch!"

She had to be dragged off the new girlfriend, but not before she had managed to rip the poor girl's blouse and skirt off her body and clawing her fingernails across the girl's face.

A week later my friend (let's call her 'Angelina', though most people call her 'Angie', for short) agreed to meet with her ex at a local bar to iron out their differences. One drink led to two, which led to three, four, five, six… and they went back to hers for old time's sake. The only thing was that Angelina 'forgot' to inform her ex (let's call him 'the Patsy') that she had had her coil taken out since they last did the nasty. I mean, what the HELL was she thinking? That she could use his sperm to try and find love? I don't for one moment excuse his behaviour in refusing to see or have anything to do with the kid whatsoever, but you can see why he feels that he was robbed. Now she's lumbered with Junior, who's the spitting image of the man she'd like to slap hard, while the CSA are currently seeking him at a forwarding address in Brazil.

Everybody knows someone like that. A few have been married to avowed non-procreators, but most have been in less stable relationships, or not in one at all, and have felt the pressure of the biological deadline. "I might just let myself get pregnant," they say. Sometimes it's a calculated ruse to tie a man more securely to them, but usually it's just because they've lost all sense of rhyme or reason and don't consider what happens afterwards.

Quite a few of these stories also have happy endings. Nature ensures a passionate bonding with baby, even for erstwhile reluctant parents, and the anger and recriminations are often forgotten for a moment. But just as often, a 'stolen' baby is not wanted by the father, even in a marriage, and the relationship breaks up. "So what," you may say, "Relationships fail all the time. You men are just trying to have your end away and avoid the consequences."

Now come on. If you happen to attract that type of man, fine, but don't dog out the rest of us. Ladies, I have had to deal with my fair share of feisty men, so I can understand how many of you feel towards every man, but the rest of us refuse to be brought down to the level of those amongst us who aren't coming correct. You get me? Pointing an accusative finger at sperm teefs should not be seen as some sign of weakness or that you're not a real woman.

In public many women will coldly say, "A condom may not be perfect, but you should still use them every time, even if you're having sex with your own wife." In private, most women will admit that they feel totally and utterly ashamed that there are so many sperm teefing sisters amongst them. I just can't understand why it is so difficult for them to admit openly that you treat others as you would want them to treat you. Behaving like an animal will have people treating you like an animal. The correlation is simple. If the vast majority of women don't start casting out the sperm teefs in their midst, men will have no choice but to treat all women with the kind of contempt that comes from not being able to trust someone with your sperm.

This lack of respect of the male sperm is becoming like an epidemic. It's time we started to ask ourselves why is this going on and why do we allow it to go on? These women are acting so terrible that they give the word ignorance a bad name. At one time, for example, you never saw women behaving like idiots while driving. Now, the prat who cuts you up or does some other rude and inconsiderate stunt, is as likely to be a woman. Ladies, stop acting ignorant. Teefing men's sperm ain't big and it ain't clever.

## HOTNESS

*Baboons in Kenya's Serengeti game reserve are reported to be suffering from stress because they now have to spend so little time foraging for food and are seldom threatened by disease or predators.*

*According to Yankee professors from Stanford University who are conducting a study, the apes suffer from stress over sexual politics, pecking orders and bullying just like humans. They are even developing symptoms such as stomach ulcers, high blood pressure and dodgy cholesterol levels. Interestingly enough, the male baboons who spent the most time grooming and being groomed by females they had no sexual interest in, and playing with infants, had the lowest levels of stress hormones.*

*Conclusion: humans can learn a lot from baboons.*

Sweetie's pregnant again!

*Surprise, surprise?*

Yeah. Thanks. But I don't know whether congratulations are in order, or whether it's commiserations. When she told me, I searched her face for that look in it that said, "It's April Fool's Day." I saw no such look. But it wasn't the right time or place for me to be saying, "Sweetie, say it's not so. It's not exactly cricket to get pregnant without discussing it. I thought you were taking precautions?"

You see, that child was conceived six weeks ago on our honeymoon and, every time I look at Sweetie, it's like I'm thinking of Bongo and that last night in Jamaica, and I become so frightened I think I'm going to poop-up meself. I dare not think about what they got up to when they disappeared on the beach. I don't want to find out. I know Sweetie's not like that. I know she's not.

It's all about trust. She's the one woman I've got to trust. I have to believe that I am the only one with a combination to her lock. I just don't know how to tell her that I hope that baby's mine, because if not I could be a grandfather sooner than I expected.

You see, after that night on the beach in Jamaica, Sweetie didn't arrive back at the hotel until minutes before we were due to leave for the airport the next morning. She arrived in style, on the back of Bongo's

CB200. He followed us all the way to the airport on it.

Bongo kept making eyes at Sweetie as we checked in. I should have thumped him, but I couldn't take my eyes off his hands, those fingers. There was little doubt. I took him to one side and quizzed him urgently about his mother, his father and his circumstances.

True, Bongo told me, his 'mudda' (as he called her) had a gold crown on her front tooth. She was married to some rich white guy and lived in a big castle outside Aberdeen. After many years of trying, she finally gave birth to Bongo, her first child, but because his "no good" black father was not around, when she met and married her husband she couldn't keep her son by another man with her because of 'politricks', so she had taken him to Jamaica as a baby to be brought up by his grandmother instead. Since then, she had given birth to an heir and a spare for the white man.

I mean, you can't tell your wife that kind of thing, can you? I couldn't very well turn to Sweetie and say, I hope you didn't bonk that rent-a-dread we met on honeymoon, 'cause I've got a feeling that he and I are related. It's not like I don't trust Sweetie. I'm just concerned, worried, terrified.

*Relax.*

How can I relax when it feels like the bottom is

dropping out of my life? How can I relax when some woman I can't recall having sex with claims that I'm the daddy to her baby? How can I relax when my woman won't have conjugal relations with me until my AIDS test comes through?

It takes years to build up trust in a relationship, and it takes only a moment of weakness to destroy it. Now Sweetie doesn't trust me. And I don't know who to trust.

I called Tonya up last night. Luckily she was still in Harlesden. Just hearing her voice made me feel ill. She claimed that she could have become pregnant during our intimate foreplay. That one sperm could have slipped out of her hands and made its way up between her thighs. "Accidents do happen."

So why didn't she let me know sooner?

She'd lost my number. "No fingers need to be pointed. We're both to blame," she argued. "You gave me a gift, a beautiful gift. Junior is a blessing."

"Gift? You can't just take my sperm and do what you want with it?"

"It *was* your sperm… Isn't it better that you know, though?"

"No. Because I'll never be a father to that child. You know that don't you? It's going to be hard on the kid."

"Life is always hard on children, whatever the

circumstances of their conception. A father is optional. I don't think it matters if you eventually fade away completely. The idea of being a single parent doesn't bother me in the least. As long as you pay your share."

I'm damned if I do and damned if I don't. As for my seed, I wonder what's going through his mind right now. I know he's only a toddler, but kids are much smarter than we give them credit for. An old work colleague, Yvette, has a son who's four. I used to pop round to see them every couple of months to pay my regards. On this occasion, like the last couple of visits, the boy acts rather strangely towards me. Getting all aggressive and trying to fight me.

His mum sent him to his room and apologised profusely. She sat down to explain that she thinks that because her son has never seen his father, he may think that I'm his papa. Her family is all in the Caribbean and her son doesn't see other males, so I can understand his confusion.

Despite her best attempts, her son doesn't quite understand the concept of an absentee father. He sees all the images on the telly about children and their dads and can't understand why he hasn't got one. To see this boy's anger and confusion is heart-breaking and it does make me wonder what kind of man would just neglect his own flesh and blood in this way.

But this boy is not alone. There are thousands of other youts who have absolutely no contact with their fathers at all. Not even for the odd weekend, Christmas etc. It's the same old cliché of man meets girl, girl gets pregnant and father disappears quicker than lead off an East End church roof.

I'm the first person to know that things happen in life that aren't exactly as you might have planned them. I'm about to be the father to a child that the stork forgot to consult with me before delivery. But children must always be seen as a blessing and, whatever the relationship you have with a child's mother, you have to do what's best for your child. Children need fathers and it's the responsibility of every father to do his best for that child.

How a man can just turn his back on his pickney and do a runner is beyond me. But it's unfortunately such a common occurrence that it's almost an expectation.

A teacher friend in Hackney tells me that the majority of kids in his class are from single parents and many of them don't seem to have much contact with their fathers. He says that these kids are the ones that have the most problems and are most disruptive.

Girls seem to cope better than boys when it comes to the lack of a father. Boys without a male role model are more affected and it seems that many end up getting into all sorts of problems in later life.

Many a single mum will try and tell you that they can do everything for a son that a man can. Well, everything except be a dad.

It's the shame of all men that so many of us do so little for our offspring. You hear all the stories and excuses from men about how the baby mother won't give them access or how the woman is the devil's daughter etc, etc. But most times this is just that, an excuse. Most women aren't going to deny access to a child and if they do, there is nothing to stop a father gaining regular access via a court order.

It's a sad experience to grow up not knowing your father, and in the long term it's a depressing feeling for a man to know that somewhere out there is his child who is despising him because he was never around.

It seems to me that women who don't inform the father about his child need to deal very seriously with that reality.

# BREAST IS BEST

*According to the New England Journal of Medicine, "Just ten minutes of staring at the charms of a well-endowed female is roughly equivalent to a thirty-minute aerobics work-out."*

*Those are the words of sexpert Dr. Karen Weatherby. Dr. Weatherby and fellow researchers at three hospitals in Frankfurt, Germany, reached the startling conclusion after comparing the health of 200 male outpatients — half of whom were instructed to look at busty females daily, the other half told to refrain from doing so.*

*The study revealed that after five years, the chest-watchers had lower blood pressure, slower resting pulse rates and fewer instances of coronary artery disease.*

*Sexual excitement gets the heart pumping and improves blood circulation," explains Dr. Weatherby.*

*"There's no question: Gazing at breasts makes men*

*healthier." Our study indicates that engaging in this activity*
*a few minutes daily cuts the risk of stroke and heart attack in*
*half. We believe that by doing so consistently, the average man*
*can extend his life by four to five years."*

For twenty years I've thought I was alone, but lately
there's been mounting evidence that it's not just me
who's lived to regret taking a woman's word.

My right to choose was really just an illusion because
a woman on a ferry, another woman in a Scottish castle
and a third woman in a house in Harlesden had already
taken the decision for me.

So what do you do if your sperm's been teefed? I
mean where can you go to report it missing? There must
be someone you can turn to.

If your mobile phone's been stolen, you go down the
nick and the old bill has a laugh at your expense while
they pretend to fill in a lot of useless forms that require a
minimum three 'A' levels to complete. I went down the
local rozzers recently to rant and rave about the teefing
little toerag who snatched my Nokia off me on the 73
bus, and the first thing the desk sergeant says to me is:
"Cor, not another one. Don't you read the papers, mate.
Right, join the back of the queue." Imagine if I went in to
report some missing sperm, they'd have a cardiac arrest.

Of course, if you had been working too hard recently and fancied a nice holiday in the sun to get away from it all but couldn't afford it, you would notify your insurance company that your house has been broken into and all your thirty-seven Nikon cameras that you were planning to give as Christmas presents, and your great-great grandmother's expensive diamonds that had been passed down from generation to generation but which you always kept well-hidden from view, had all been swiped.

Not only that, if you yourself got nicked for smoking ganja on the streets of Brixton, you'd call your missus on the mobile and notify her that you'll be ten minutes late for dinner and you'll probably have a big appetite when you get home.

But if your sperm's been stolen, where can you go? Well, you'll be surprised to know that there isn't a single government agency that you can turn to. I couldn't believe this so I turned to the Child Support Agency who, after all, know a lot about tracing down genetic material. It's the CSA that is making men pay for children they didn't know they were fathering. I went to see the minister in charge, Baroness Hollis, to ask her how that can be right. I also wanted to find out how the government distinguishes between fathers who are just trying to run away from their obligations and those dads who, I think, were victims of sperm theft.

I donned a new suit and buffed up my shoes and went down to their offices in Whitehall (right across the road from Downing Street), armed with 'Exhibit A' (a handful of Polaroid pics of the relevant sperm bandits in the nude).

On my arrival, Baroness Hollis escorted me through those daunting corridors of power to her office and sat me down. I told her my stories (leaving out the horny bits).

"It would be funny, except that stray sperm in the stolen semen met up with eggs that shouldn't have been there in the first place. Now, I'm not looking to have these women hung, drawn and quartered for their banditry, all I'm asking is for someone to say that I was the wronged party," I explained.

She was having none of it. Like she had heard it all before she fired back, "So who do you think should pay for your kids, other people's fathers? Is that what you're saying?"

It was like she hadn't been listening. "This isn't about money," I insisted, "but how can men be expected to accept responsibility for decisions which they weren't involved in? And what are you going to do about all these women who are going around teefing a man's

# The sperm

She wants a baby, she gets pregnant 'by accident'. It probably happens all the time
**Sarah Litvinoff**. Do fathers really matter so little?

*AND I THOUGHT IT WAS LOVE THAT SHE WANTED*

**GONE!**

A teaspoonful of liquid has once again found itself at the centre of a courtroom battle. First there was the case of the woman who fought through the courts to be allowed to impregnate herself with her dead husband's semen. Now there's the misappropriation of Peter Wallis's precious elixir of life. All he wanted to do was have sex, for goodness sake, and Kellie Smith breached their contract by "intentionally acquiring and misusing his semen".

What's a man to do – especially in the United States – but sue? And what's a woman to do, except hire some clever lawyers to argue that Peter's ejaculate was a gift, and that he "surrendered any right of possession to his semen when he transferred it during voluntary sexual intercourse"?

It would be funny, except that a stray sperm in the stolen semen met up with an egg that shouldn't have been there in the first place, and the result was one-year-old Taylor Smith. Whichever parent wins, the little girl loses. How heartwarming to grow up to discover that your mother tricked your father (or not, as Kellie maintains) and that he felt so "shocked" and "betrayed" that he went to law to make sure that everyone knew he didn't want you.

The only new aspect in this story is the legal battle about the alleged breach of contract (he was given the impression that she was using effective contraception). Otherwise, countless women with a yen for a baby have used a man purportedly for sex, but really for procreation (his story). And countless other women have been "shocked" themselves when contraception fails (her story). Quite a few of these stories also have happy endings. After nine months the result is a fetching little creature: nature ensures a passionate bonding, even for erstwhile reluctant parents, and the anger and recriminations are often forgotten.

But just as often, a "stolen" baby is not wanted by the father, even in a marriage, and the relationship breaks up. So what? you may say. Relationships fail all the time. It's always going to be hard on the kids, whatever the circumstances of their conception.

I used to subscribe to the view that a father was an optional extra. In fact, when I made the best mistake of my life and became pregnant when I was 19 (not remotely on purpose), I knew that my relationship with my daughter's father – my first boyfriend – wouldn't last, and I didn't think it mattered if he eventually faded away completely. The idea of being a single parent didn't bother me in the least. And we did, indeed, break up before she was two.

My cavalier attitude to the importance of the father was slightly before its time (25 years ago). Now it's commonplace. You have the celebrity ex-

tings? It ain't funny and it ain't clever."

"It's no good crying about it now," she continued, "you were willing to take the risk and suffer the consequences later. But I get back to my point, who do you think should pay for your children, other people's fathers?"

"So what, are you only interested in the biological facts of fatherhood?" I asked incredulously. "Do you mean that the circumstances of how the sperm came to be there in the first place, to fertilize the egg, is irrelevant?"

"As far as we're concerned, yes. You can't expect the government to interfere in what goes on between two people in the bedroom. No matter how women become pregnant, the biological fathers are responsible in the eyes of the law. And it's right that they should pay. Or are you suggesting that other people's fathers should pay?"

"But clearly some women think that ejaculation is a freebie. Surely the government wants to send out a message to those women that it's not. Semen is property. Surely some crime has been committed?"

"A crime may or may not have been committed, that's a matter you can take up with the civil courts. But you have no legal right not to become a parent. To men at risk of 'entrapment', we say, use a condom. Men should take equal responsibility for preventing pregnancy."

Now hold on a second, a ragamuffin from Tottenham I may be, but even I can smell something fishy here. "Do you mean to say, Baroness Hollis, that if my car is stolen outside my house and someone uses it to go and rob a bank that I am responsible for the money that's been stolen from that bank?"

"No, of course not. But your insurance company might find you negligent for not locking your car properly."

"Yes, but the money being stolen from the bank, the end result, I'm innocent of that charge."

"Look, this isn't about money being stolen from a bank, it's about children."

"I agree, that's why it's even more important to make sperm napping a serious crime. If a woman broke into my house and nicked my telly I'd call the police on her. If she mashed up my car, she'd be getting a letter from my lawyers. How can it be all right for her to nick my sperm to have a child? And then — to make matters worse — deny me any rights to have anything to do with it. Why should I be expected to suffer what effectively amounts to theft and psychological damage with no recourse to action? I can't even live my own life because I know that some kid I've never seen and don't know anything about might come knocking on my door. Why should I suffer the slings and arrows of outrageous fortune that come with being duped into fathering a child?"

Baroness Hollis wasn't impressed. She refuses to call for spermnapping to be made a criminal offence, or for the CSA to regard lack of consent to be an extenuating circumstance in cases. She isn't making any allowances for men who say that they have become unwitting fathers. She says, 'tell it to the judge'. But what will the courts say to a man who says he's been a victim of sperm crime?

I went to see legal expert Dr. Sally Sheldon, senior law lecturer at Keele University. She's been so struck by this 'phenomenon' that she's been doing research on it, and she suggested I 'tell it' to an American judge, because I was likely to have a more sympathetic hearing over there than over here. She's looked at cases where men did go to the courts to claim mitigating circumstances, and the results are hardly encouraging.

"English law doesn't recognize the crime of sperm theft," she told me. "As it currently stands, the law only cares about identifying fathers and making them pay."

The law is out of date.

The government is out of touch.

It's Catch 22. The government tells me to go the law. The law tells me that I'm just the price paid for a principle which is increasingly out of step with how we live now. The law only seems to care about identifying fathers and making them pay.

It's time to take this campaign to the streets. I may be a one man band but something's got to be done. I want to persuade people that men are the victims here. If sperm bandits won't hear when men say 'no', we'll have to shout it out loud. The time has come to stand and be counted, for men to act — to get back the rights over our sperm and how it is used!

I'm going to start by taking my case to the media.

# HOME IS WHERE THE HURT IS

- *1pk Cornflakes*
- *2 loaves of sunflower bread*
- *1 tin of chopped tomatoes*
- *1 bag of potatoes*
- *10 kilo bag of rice*
- *1 bunch of bananas*
- *1 kilo of apples*
- *1 large box of washing powder*
- *1 copy of Reader's Wives*

Sweetie's getting fatter every day. I'm getting more and more tense by the hour. The longest that I have gone without the sweet nectar of a woman's bosom would be nine months. Talk about a dry spell, those were some sorry times! Nine months, two weeks and three days to be precise. I don't ever want to go that long again. I'm telling you, dem was some tense months. It was during the great pum-pum famine of '97, when I had to call upon some swift international aid because I had been so badly hurt by my ex that I really couldn't find anybody I wanted to do it with. Half of that time I didn't even have an appetite for it, but when I did…

I know what you're thinking — men are obsessed with not being committed. I've got to admit, fidelity isn't easy when your woman is holding back on the fun and games. At least I'm being honest. That's better than me going around being grumpy every friggin' day because I can't get sex off my mind, even when I'm sleeping. At the supermarket. At the gym. Wherever. I know, I need to focus on intellectual pursuits instead, so I can attain knowledge, wisdom, understanding. Confucius say, 'It is your lot in life. Embrace it. Love it. Be one with it. Man who not getting sex from wife, beat penis very much.'

Women often cause a man to stray. A woman who stops making an effort to impress her man, for example. If she was wearing nice clothes, looking and smelling good when she first met him, and she starts slacking after some time in the relationship, then it's that woman's fault if his roving eye starts roving. If when he met her she was one size, and after some time with her

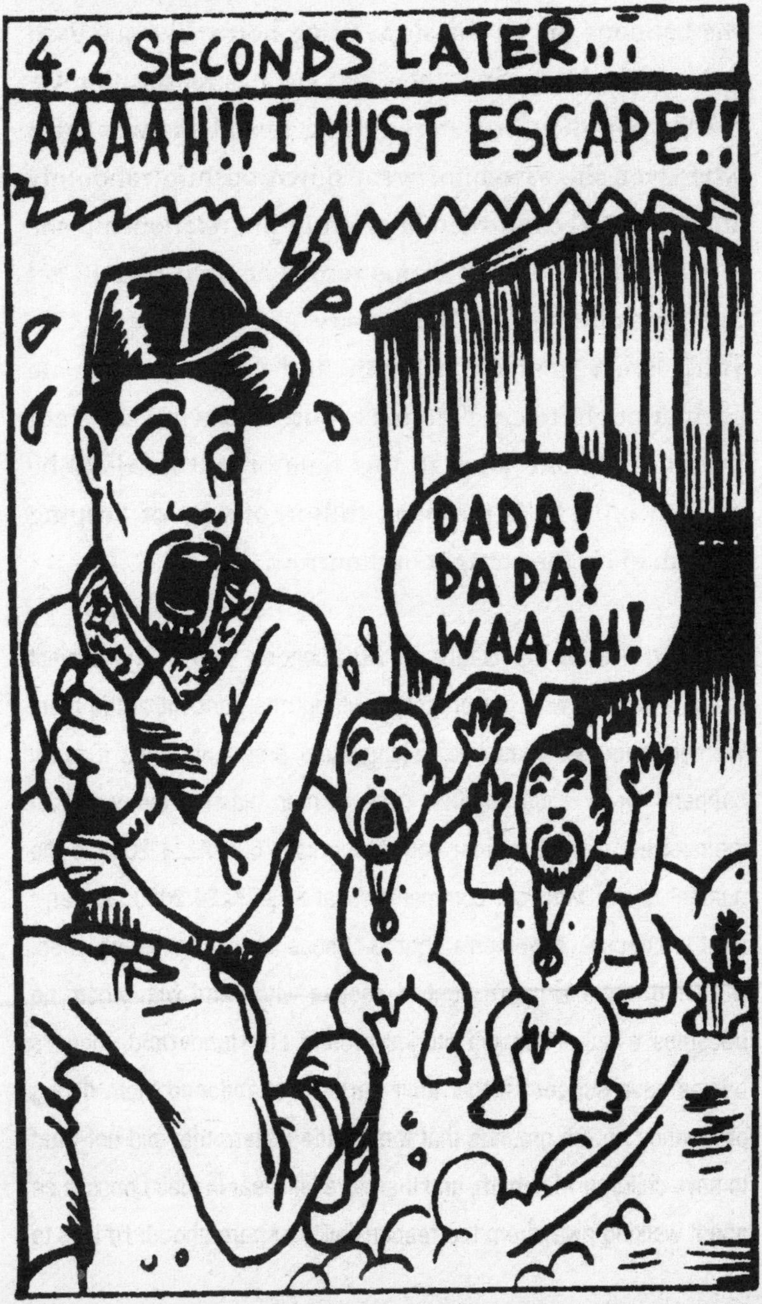
4.2 SECONDS LATER...
AAAAH!! I MUST ESCAPE!!
DADA! DA DA! WAAAH!

she balloons up, or she stops being horny like she used to be in the beginning, then that eye has reason to rove. Like, when they first start getting sexual she wanted it whenever she saw him, went down on him randomly and frequently, but then later on in the relationship she kinda quits. You can't blame him if he then tries to get this pleasure back in somebody else's bedroom. Can you? Every married woman and long-term female partner ought to check to make sure that what she's got is still 'da boom' after all this time or if it needs to be worked on. That's the most full-proof way of keeping your man on the straight and narrow.

GAUNTY: This is Jon Gaunt, at BBC London 94.9... The subject today is women who get pregnant without the consent of the man. Women who trick men into getting them pregnant. Does it really happen? Or is it just another case of men blaming everyone but themselves? I want to hear your thoughts... 020 7224 2000 is the number to call with your comments. That's 020 7224 2000. 'A man's right to choose'. A woman's right to choose is now well established. But what about a man's right to choose when and with whom he becomes a father? Media stories around Liz Hurley and Jordan's babies have suggested that their partners abandoned them during pregnancy on the grounds that they made it clear they did not want to have children with them, and therefore felt clear in their conscience about walking away from the responsibility of parenthood. I'd love to get your calls on the subject. With me is D, a thirtysomething married man from north London with two young daughters and... possibly a few more kids out there. Tell us your story. How did you get in this mess?

D: Just one little sperm, that's all it took, Gaunty. One little sperm taken without my permission on a slow boat to Sweden twenty years ago. I was robbed. Mugged. You can't behave like that in a civilised society. Yet there are no laws against it. It's outrageous. I've been through all the law books, and nowhere does it talk about a man's right to choose. I said no, and I meant no. No kids. N. O. It's my sperm, but I've got no rights over it. It's like anybody can come along, teef it, and hand it back to me fully grown. I want my goods returned to me in the same condition they were in when they left me. Pure and simple. It's time we established some ground rules. Time that we got some real communication going on. It doesn't matter whether I'm just checking a girl in a dance or I'm about to move in with her, let's get it clear and in the open what we both want from this relationship. You see, unless I specifically state that I'm in the procreation game, I think it's probably safer to assume that I'm not looking to become a father to your child.

GAUNTY: Well, that's D's view. I'm sure you'll want to respond to that. The number once again is 020 7224 2000. That's 020 7224 2000. The Jon Gaunt Show on BBC London... Got an e-mail here from

Vicky, who's listening to us on the web from Boston, in the United States... this is addressed to you, D... 'You dummy, of course it's your fault. You should have used a condom'... now, how do you respond to that?

D: Well, Vicky, I can give you an example here in England where a man used a condom and the woman he was having sex with went and took the sperm out of the condom and impregnated herself with it. So, a condom can't save you. The truth is that if a woman doesn't want to get pregnant there is no way she's going to get pregnant. Which man wouldn't use a condom if the woman asked him to? But if she says it's okay, she's taking care of business and I don't have to wear a condom, I'm not expecting to get an 'oh dear, I'm pregnant' call two months later. It's her body. She knows what she's doing.

WOMAN CALLER 1: I am so irritated by the bloke you've got on air. I mean, how can you be putting the blame on women?

D: Hang on. Let's be honest here. Women make the rules in this game. A man can go and chat up a woman but she's the one who decides whether you're going to have sex or not. Most guys are willing to do almost anything for sex.

WOMAN CALLER 1: Then wear a condom. Nobody's stopping you.

D: I agree. Or better still, stay celibate. F'real doh, it takes a strong man to resist temptation. No matter how strong you are, how committed you are, your instincts lurk just beneath the surface waiting for just one moment's weakness. And if you are in a relationship and you are having sex, you can't keep wearing a condom for ever, can you? What about all these married men who don't want any more kids. How is it that all these pregnancies are happening when a man is making it perfectly clear that he's not in the market for any more pickney? Think of all the four-parent families out there who would only be three parent families if the missus had listened when her hubby said 'no more'. If she had listened, they'd be able to drive around in an ordinary saloon car instead of the ugly monstrosity they are having to pollute our roads with. It's all about trust. Men have to be able to take a woman's word. Because otherwise we'd have to assume that any woman we sleep with is a potential sperm bandit.

WOMAN CALLER 2: It's terrible to think a woman would behave like this, but I'm surprised that you didn't take any precautions nevertheless.

1st MALE CALLER: What I'd like to ask, D is, how come there are so many children out there who came from that one last drink after the break up of a relationship?

2nd MALE CALLER: And it's not just one night stands. How many guys out there are trapped in a marriage now, just because their long-term girlfriend who they didn't want a kid with got pregnant?

3rd MALE CALLER: Sperm wars, that's what it is. The mother of all sperm wars.

4th MALE CALLER: There's only one explanation — women are making the decision to get pregnant without us knowing. And that is not on. All I wanted to do was have sex, for goodness sake. I mean, ladies, men who pick you up in a bar are obviously not looking for a relationship.

5th MALE CALLER: It is a modern day tragedy that the gap between male and female beliefs is seemingly as wide as the Grand Canyon. Why women don't try and bridge the gap and attempt to move a little closer in their understanding of the male state of mind is beyond me.

WOMAN CALLER 3: I'd just like to say to D that this is your daughter Rebecca's seventh birthday. You might want to send a request out to her and wish her many happy returns of the day...

Rebecca? *Me?* No. No. NOOOOOooooooooo!!!!!

# LOVEBOX

*Malcolm returns from the doctor and tells his wife, Cynthia, that the doctor has told him he has only 24 hours to live. Given this prognosis, Malcolm asks Cynthia for sex. Naturally, she agrees, and they 'get busy'.*

*About six hours later, Malcolm goes to Cynthia and says, "Baby, you know say how I have only eighteen hours to live, could we please just do it one more time?"*

*Cynthia agrees and they do it again.*

*Later, as Malcolm gets into bed, he looks at his watch and realises that he now has only eight hours left. He touches Cynthia's shoulder and asks, "Baby, please... just one more time before I die."*

*She says, "Of course, Big Daddy," and they make love for the third time.*

*After this session, Cynthia rolls over and falls asleep.*

*Malcolm, however, worried about his impending death, tosses and turns until he's down to four hours. He taps Cynthia. "Baby, I have only four more hours. Do you think we could..."*

*At this point Cynthia sits up and says, "Listen, I have to get up in the morning. You don't!"*

My hour on Gaunty's show proves that not everybody thinks I'm in the wrong. Though my proposal that sperm bandits should be treated the same way as drunk drivers and banned from having sex for a year or two was perhaps too radical for some of the trendy types that called in, who seem to think that being a caveman is a very undesirable state of mind. But I am encouraged to know that I am not alone, that here are so many men out there who became fathers against their will. But no one's saying anything. I can't keep quiet any longer. I've got to speak out. To get my message out I'm going to shout it out loud from the rooftops. It's time to take this campaign to the people.

It's not easy finding a soap box nowadays. There isn't much call for them. There aren't too many places left where you can get up on your soap box and tell it like it is without being sectioned. Thank goodness for Speaker's Corner then. I went down there last Sunday with milk crate and the banner I'd been up all night painting: HANDS OFF THE SPERM.

"Ladies, and gentlemen, friends and... I see some enemies... I do not come to diss women, but to praise them... but there are some women who are *dyam* outta order. You know who I'm talking about, the sperm bandits — sperm teefs. We all know one or two — women who have breached the sex contract by intentionally acquiring and misusing our semen. I didn't think anyone could stoop so low. Twenty years ago someone stole my sperm and used it without my consent. In my book, that's robbery, but as far as the law's concerned, no crime has been committed. We hear a lot about feckless fathers and absent dads. But what about the men whose sperm has been used without their permission — or who don't even know they're dads until a stranger comes knocking at their door? No one knows how many of us there are. It's happening all around us and all we ever hear is the story of men who ducked their responsibilities, who walked out, or who were never there in the first place. I've decided to go on the warpath against the sperm bandits. It's time to get tough on the sperm thief and tough on the the causes of sperm theft.

"Ladies, is there something we're doing to give you the impression we want a child with you? Because I think that's something that kind of needs to be agreed upfront. How many of you have been in a relationship with a man and assumed that he wants a child but is maybe just too shy to admit it? Well, let me suggest that in future it would be polite to check with him first.

"All we want is the same rights as women. Imagine if somehow you could steal, impregnate and grow a woman's egg. Imagine how she would feel if she was presented with a three year old child she didn't know about!

"I'd like to highly-recommend a book on the subject — *Sperm Wars*. It's by Dr. Robin Baker. He reckons that women are more likely to conceive when they know it's their last chance to get the boom semen — high-calibre, good genetic material. It's all right here in the book:

" *'Only wealthy mean will be able to afford to have children with a number of women, and hence only such men will be targeted by many women. Poorer men, when they do get a chance to inseminate extra women, will be under pressure to make themselves even more untraceable than at present... nothing will prevent a woman from subconsciously trying to collect the best genes and recruit the best support for her children that her genes and circumstances will allow.'*

"If I say no to kids, I mean no. When a man says no we REALLY mean no. Unless we say it in a seductive way... 'nooooooo... heee-heeee... stoooppp... heeehee… nooooooo'. And if women won't listen when men say 'no', maybe they'll listen when we say 'fraud', 'misappropriation' 'theft'?

"When you buy a house the law doesn't allow you to just buy it on the spot. It requires that you exchange contracts, giving you time to reflect before completion. Even buying a car takes a bit of thought and planning. You want to get married? Fine. But first you've got to post up banns for weeks. So when you want a child, the same care, thought and attention should be applied. It's time we established some ground rules. It's time that we got some real communication going on. It doesn't matter whether I'm just checking a girl in a dance or I'm about to move in with her, let's just get it clear what we both want from this relationship. Let's put it down on paper. A contract. Get a lawyer to witness it. Then maybe people will give a second thought before they commit fraud:

"We had a perfect marriage until his girlfriend started dating my boyfriend!"

## PRE-COITAL AGREEMENT

### (To be completed and signed by both parties)

"I_____ (insert man's name) would like to have sex with ____
(insert woman's name) and that this constitutes an agreement or
intention on the part of _____ (insert man's name) to marry
____ (insert woman's name).

____ (insert woman's name) does not consent to have sex with
____ (insert man's name) under any other circumstances. I
accept that sex with ____ (insert woman's name) under any other
circumstances is sex without her consent.

Signed

_____ (female)

_____ (male)

_____ (witness)

### PRE-COITAL AGREEMENT 2
#### (To be completed and signed by both parties)

"I_____ (insert man's name) would like to have sex with ____ (insert woman's name) and that this in NO WAY constitutes an agreement or intention on the part of _____ (insert man's name) to marry ____ (insert woman's name).

____ (insert woman's name) consents to have sex with ____ (insert man's name) under any circumstances. ____ (insert woman's name accepts that sex with ____ (insert man's name) is sex without any strings attached.

**Signed**

_____ (female)
_____ (male)
_____ (witness)

## PRE-COITAL AGREEMENT 3

### (To be completed and signed by both parties)

"I_____ (insert man's name) would like to have sex with ____ (insert woman's name) and that this constitutes an agreement or intention on the part of _____ (insert man's name) to have children with ____ (insert woman's name).

____ (insert woman's name) consents to have sex with ____ (insert man's name) on the understanding that if ____ (insert woman's name) gets pregnant ____ (insert man's name) will have no rights whatsoever over the child.

**Signed**

_____ (female)

_____ (male)

_____ (witness)

## PRE-COITAL AGREEMENT 4
### (To be completed and signed by both parties)

"I_____ (insert man's name) would like to have sex with ____
(insert woman's name) and that this in NO WAY constitutes an
agreement or intention on the part of _____ (insert man's
name) to have children with ____ (insert woman's name).

____ (insert man's name) consents to have sex with ____ (insert
woman's name) on the understanding that she will take all
necessary precautions not to get pregnant and that if ____
(insert woman's name) gets pregnant ____ (insert man's name)
will have the right to sue her in a court of law for emotional
stress etc.
Signed

_____ (female)
_____ (male)

_____ (witness)


I distributed the contract out amongst those gathered to hear my speech. As I was about to return to my milk crate a girl of about fourteen came up to me and said, "Dad?"

*Aaaaaaaaaaaaaaarrrrrgggghhh!*

Standing right behind her were two other girls who were identical to her.

# EPILOGUE

*From flights to wedding dresses to mobile phones. Richard Branson's empire gets more diverse by the day. Nowadays all companies with a successful brand name are looking at ways of maximising their earning potential. When you have an earth moving vehicle company like Caterpillar with its name on clothing, then you know that anything is possible.*

*For companies wishing to expand their empires, the condom market would be an ideal one. Millions are sold every year and, excuse the expression, the tooling costs are small compared with other products. They could even use their existing adverts to cut costs. The following are just a few examples:*

*Nike Condoms — Just do it*

*Peugeot Condoms — The ride of your life*

*Sony Condoms — Do not underestimate the power*

*Microsoft Condoms — Where do you want to go today?*

*KFC Condoms — Finger Licking Good*

*Safeway Condoms — Lightening the Load*

*Abbey National Condoms — 'Cause life's complicated enough*

*Coca Cola Condoms — The Real Thing*

*Ever Ready Condoms — Keep going and going …*

*Pringles Condoms — Once you pop, you can't stop*

*Burger King Condoms- Home of the Whopper*

*Philips Condoms — Let's make things better*

*BT Condoms — Stay in touch*

Have you ever been at a party or other social function and can count at least five women there that you have been with? Have you ever gotten a female's phone number and then realised that you have already had sex with her before?

It was fifteen years ago, at a New Year' Eve party in a huge loft in Hackney. It was my first night out in about four months so I was determined to have a nice time. The place was roadblocked with horny looking women all willing to just hand it over (and there I was thinking 'I'm going to do my damndest to control it this year'). But I got so pissed my head was spinning. Or was it the girl in the PVC catsuit rubbing herself up against my crotch?

*Gotta stay focused. Gotta stay focused. Gotta have a slash.*

Someone shouted in my ear, "You're off your tree, mate. You know that? I want some of what you're on."

I rushed to the bathroom and emptied the contents of my stomach. I lifted my head from under the tap and looked in the mirror to make sure I was still alive before returning to the party and getting drunk all over again. I couldn't help myself.

Anyway, one moment I'm chilling with a few beers and the next thing I know I'm knee deep in pum-pum. I swear, that's how it happened — knee deep!

I had passed out on a bed. That's how drunk I was (I don't usually behave like this in other people's houses, y'know). As I slept, I dreamed that the woman in the catsuit was in the bed with me and we were making love on rose petals, and I'm thinking, 'Damn, you are sexier than I imagined'. I filled every inch of her with my deep thrust, slipping in and out of her pulsating lips, quenching her thirst with my hot throbbing juices, for about ninety minutes, until she couldn't take it anymore. It gives me the shivers just thinking about it. Don't know about wet dreams, but I got a little moist, I must admit. I'm getting a little moist now just thinking about it.

Then I started slowly waking up, and there she was again, pumping up and down on top of me.

I almost crapped myself. She had stripped my clothes

off while I was dozing and was having her wicked way with me.

"Remember me?" she smiled, as my eyes tried to focus. "I thought you were dead."

Yes, I was dead. Dead to the world. Too drunk to know whether it really happened or not.

But the CSA say it did and are sending me a bill for the fourteen year old triplets I never knew I had.


There is a cause and effect to a man's anger. Women, on the other hand, sometimes get angry for no discernable logical reason. You'd think there was a little dude in their heads that says, 'Hey, it's Tuesday around noon, let's be in a bad mood right now.'

Take Sweetie for instance, I don't know whether this unexpected pregnancy is to blame, but she's thrown me out of the home that I sweat blood and tears for. Says I can see the kids at the weekend. And all because some woman left a text message on my mobile saying *CNGRTS ITS YR GRNDSON'S FIRST B'DAY XXXX JENNY.*

Jenny? JENNY? I don't know a Jenny. *Grandson?* That's a laugh. There must be some mistake.

The tension and headaches are starting to take their toll on me. I'm shaking like a leaf all over. I would like to have all this ugliness go away so I can get back to being a father and raising my two 'legitimate' daughters in peace.

Maybe I'll send Sweetie some flowers. Knowing her she'll probably trash them. Why have I always got to be the one to say sorry?

She says she's through with talking, like that's all we've been doing for years. If two grown folk can't come to some meeting of the mind after something like this, then something's wrong.

So I'm living in a bedsit in Tottenham, back in the ghetto again, wondering if I'm stuck in a nightmare in some parallel universe. I'm having to fight over washing machines with Somalians and Albanian refugees — again. I'm forever cooking and cleaning and ironing. I'm aching all over — my arms, my legs... Uh, I'm not going to say what else is aching and why.

## END